WRITTEN IN PROTEST

Written in Protest
Edited by Anjali Sethi
Print Edition

First Published & Printed in India in 2021
Inkfeathers Publishing
New Delhi 110095, India

Copyright © Inkfeathers Publishing, 2021
Book & Cover Design © 2021 Inkfeathers Publishing

www.inkfeathers.com

WRITTEN IN PROTEST

Here lie, the tales of the battles we cannot afford to lose

Edited & Compiled by

Anjali Sethi

Inkfeathers Publishing

DISCLAIMER

The anthology "Written in Protest" is a collection of stories, poems, and articles by 51 authors who belong to different parts of the globe. The anthology editor and the publisher have edited the content provided by the co-authors to enhance the experience for readers and made it free of plagiarism as much as possible. All the stories, poems, and articles published in this anthology are a work of fiction. Unless otherwise indicated, all the names, characters, objects, businesses, places, events, incidents- whether physical/non-physical, real/unreal, tangible/ intangible in whatsoever description used in this book are either the product of the author's imagination or used in a fictitious manner. Any resemblance to actual persons, objects, entities, living or dead, or actual events is purely coincidental. The stories, poems and articles published in this book are solely owned by their respective authors and are no way intended to hurt anyone's religious, political, spiritual, brand, personal or fanatic beliefs and/or faith, whatsoever. All the brand names mentioned in this book (if any) are the properties of their respective owners which do not endorse this book in any way.

In case, any sort of plagiarism is detected in the stories, poems, and articles within this anthology or in case of any complaints or grievances or objections, neither the anthology editor, nor the publisher are to be held responsible for any such claims. The author(s) who holds the rights to the particular story, poem, or article, shall be held responsible, whatsoever.

CO-AUTHORED BY

Alexis M. Romo ~ Aparna Goswami ~ Ann Chaiti Sarkar ~ Alison Hawes ~ Arti Chopra ~ Annika Hauer ~ Aeryn Perez ~ Arunanshu Deep ~ Bethany Rose Castle ~ Charlene Rosario ~ Divya Bora ~ Deepika Bhardwaj ~ Debjani Saha ~ Emily Alexander ~ Eileen Salisbury ~ Uniliar ~ Harshita Garrepalli ~ Heer Dayani ~ Jagruthi Kommuri ~ Jacqueline Olivia ~ Jennifer Meyers ~ Jesika Gaston ~ Kristina Kerber ~ Kriti ~ Mythili M. U ~ Madhurya Kommuri ~ Marissa Kovalenko ~ Noela Paraschiv ~ Nagasri MN ~ Noelle Nams ~ Neha Mazumder ~ Omaira Mahan ~ Padmini Peteri ~ Robert Ormsby ~ Rhea Choudhury ~ Sybil Samuel ~ Shama Mahajan ~ s.h. ~ Shakira Washington ~ Skyler Saunders ~ Shaymi Shah ~ Swati Thapa ~ Sharron Green ~ Snehal Agarwal ~ Sameem Hassain Mohammad ~ Tanisha Thalnerkar ~ Tolulope Ibiyode ~ Tiffany Lindfield ~ Usama Bin Tanveer ~ Urmi Chakraborty ~ Yashika Tomar

CONTENTS

STORIES

POEMS

ARTICLES

POEMS

ABOUT THE EDITOR

ANJALI SETHI

Anjali Sethi is an ambitious eighteen-year-old who raises her voice against dire issues that she feels strongly about. Her words document her experiences and protest in the form of poetry and prose. Her work has been published in several anthologies through various national and international publishing houses. Besides this, she is fascinated by the human mind and feels strongly against the patriarchal society and the stigma surrounding mental health. She continues to educate herself and spread awareness about the LGBTQIA+ Community and holds a firm stance as a feminist. You can find glimpses of her work on Instagram @theunmaskedwriter and on her blog: www.theunmaskedwriter.wordpress.com.

EDITOR'S NOTE

This book began when thought met action.

We live in a world that is protesting day in and day out. Starting from climate change, pollution, and the extinction of species, where our motherland screams for mercy; to racism, sexism, and undemocratic acts of exclusion, where our people scream for mercy – somewhere in the middle, we lost sight of humanity. This, for years and years, has been a part and parcel of our lives, with a few brave-hearts who made a difference, and some who were silenced.

Evidently, this fight didn't just begin. From people like Andrée de Jongh, Martha Gellhorn, Florynce Rae Kennedy, Martin Luther King, Frederick Douglass, and so many more, we have learnt about this revolution; and for that revolution, we stand united. We may be from different cultures and backgrounds, and have different ideas of development in our minds, but collectively, we stand against social evils. We stand for a better, more inclusive world.

From the Pride movement, the Black Lives Matter movement, to the Dalit Lives Matter movement, regardless of geographical boundaries, we have learnt to hand the mic over. To let those voices that have been repressed for ages, take over and incite change. We stand against the forces to protect our people who need to be in the spotlight. We speak of our support for them and we stand with them as allies.

In this book, you will find such wonderful members and allies of the Pride movement, the Dalit Lives Matter movement, the Black Lives Matter movement, the Feminist movement, and many more. Above all, you will observe what Florynce Rae Kennedy spoke passionately about- intersectionality, come to life in these pages.

You will hear the blood curdling screams and cries of our people – their pain, their sorrow, their frustration; but, also, their gratefulness, joy and love for their fellow people and their accomplishments in this protest. You will celebrate with us, you will scream with us, and you will mourn for our lost warriors with us.

The road will seem bumpy but bear with us. When I embarked on this journey, I was uncertain of what I had set out to do, but as time passed, I found solace in the words of the writers in this anthology. Their drive, determination, constant encouragement, support, and kindness reaffirmed my faith in the change that I, and so many others, wish to bring. This anthology explores that fight, that every one of these wonderful writers have been through, and continue to go through, to make a difference around them.

It is awing — their dedication, their strength and the growth that is reflected in their words.

I hope you find some solace, an abundance of ardour and motivation through their words, as I have from bringing these prolific writers together.

Anjali Sethi
Editor

POEMS

Free

by Charlene Rosario

They stand in opposition, unmoving, accusatory.
We hold our heads high, matching their gaze, resolute.
"After all these years, tell us, are we truly free?"
"Indeed, you have a voice and a vote, your rights absolute.

Thus, they preach brazenly of what they call freedom
And perhaps they're right, we merely couldn't comprehend
A state with disguised misdeeds against which we keep mum.
With an idea of faux freedom we'll go along, we'll pretend.

"We're free, yes, we believe that with unwavering certainty.
Our brothers and sisters, they're free indeed,
Free to take a promenade, then get shot in the street,
Free to be unfairly judged, slapped, so surely, with a penalty.
Charged on suspicion and for not being white, beaten."

So, you can keep your notion of what freedom is supposed be.
With friends of all colours, we'll stand our ground, hand in hand.
Our cries, our chants will not go unheard, neither will our legacy.
Our daughters and our sons, all together, they'll rebuild this land.

And the earth, she'll sing as she celebrates the end of supremacy.

I Have Made Art from Decay

by Urmi Chakraborty

I refuse to disappear into thin air
My being is so strong that it can condense into clouds
Rain with the grains of heaven from above.

I am the flowers of evil
I may have cut my skin
Broken my epidermal tissues
Burnt my heart with rage
But I have bolts of hair
Like tree roots in the endless skies
I can search for meaning
I can search for translation
I can search for hope.

I couldn't tell heaven from hell.
I shuddered on the minefield of
societal subtleties,
My head ripped from my heart
I refused to live a life
In graveyards of choices.

My legs are survivors
I kept running and following drumbeats,
But they died in the face of my eye.
I've been pushed, and pushed so hard

I couldn't conceal my agony
I teared up, I teared apart
I made a mistake, I denied myself.
Now I open my chest and pull out my veins,
I see voices flowing
A revolution of the blood
I keep digging myself
I bend sunlight into my soul
I breathe in the air,
I have made art from decay.

Bangla Road

by Emily Alexander

sunken eyes glazed with drugs and denial
sweat dripping over bared breasts
her dignity painfully packed beneath desperation
she chose this he thinks
and wrecks her body as she bleeds
her mind numbed by a cycle with no escape
forgotten to the pleasures of the privileged
the acceptable rape
she is human too

a beautiful soul born to a broken body
not compassion given but disdain
abandoned and alone
confidence crushed because her legs do not work
for nothing but a good laugh
she is human too

he leaves his wife at the break of night
to give himself to men
a closed mind lost deep in her eyes
the strength to live this pain
freeing his baby from the same fate
he is human too

and so the crowds continue
both the entitled and depraved
a place where forbidden pleasure
floats to the surface of conscience
humanity deserted in the name of fun
see their faces and hear their voices
broken by confines of culture
the value of their lives will not be forsaken
for we are human too

Why Do Fireworks Not Light The Sky

by Uniliar

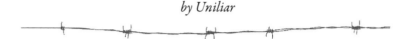

Countless grains of soil lying upon coffins of innocents,
merely trying to live their life but gaping holes are punctured
through their body, letting warmth leak right out of them.
Children cowering under tables and chairs, behind walls,
their cries are silenced for the safety of their life.
And yet, they continue to hide in paranoia, which day,
which school, is it going to be next?

From head to foot they are covered in shields, faces masked
and we can only guess their identity,
letting a court excuse the cold-blooded murder of others,
like laws are just another useless lecture.
I wonder if they have forgotten the face of their father,
the voice of their mother.

Look up to the sky when the clouds are all a little bit faded
conjoined with every colour and the world seems so free.
Except all these wisps are just shades of grey,
pictures of a never-ending storm.
Breathing in fumes of fired bullets covered in red iron.
Is it so bad to be different? A darker swatch that still runs
the same colour blood. What about the missing pieces of futures?
Stolen in a heartbeat from the hands of a child.

Who are they to decide that the sky should be lit with stains of
shrapnel shells?

Matter

by Kristina Kerber

Polluted politicians decisively devise
To divide diversified daughters and sons
Like a scientific skyline divides dust and dawn,
Devaluating discernment fuelled by effortless ease,
Creating a monochrome chessboard.
Don't they teach in school
That life is not a game of chess?
This neither a matter of perspective
Nor a matter of time,
It's a matter of fact that those who matter count,
Not once have I met someone
Who mattered none.
In a world where love is love is love
Universal acceptance is substantially lacking.
Skin upon skin should be sinless
As long as loving souls are united.

Made With Melanin

by Debjani Saha

Hate and prejudice
once made love in the cold air
under the dead sky
devoid of stars
furious and naked
rolling in atrocious pleasure
gave birth to a thought
swallowed in darkness.
An absurd bigotry walked the face of the earth for the very first time.

Blind and shallow,
tongue like a pitchfork
a deadly king of the Basilisks
this hate child speaks fluent spleen
to the innocent shadows
of men and women
fogging mirrors of their soul
with "coloured" lores.

Intolerance your sinned sibling,
a social cancer for the healthy living.
As you breathe disgust and judgement,
a sin inherited from your forefathers.

For their skin is theirs to love fiercely without any apology.
Too resilient and striking
this melanin is like dark honey.
So, rise and shout now
my brothers and sisters.
Scream, "We are black"
with all your might.
For it is time, to shine again.
For it is time, to be a newly lit star
to a dying sky.

Unification

by Tolulope Ibiyode

Through many generations,
we've seen huge segregation
based on skin pigmentation.
Enough of the oppression,
it's time for a revolution.
No more division,
it's not profitable to us as a whole.
The new direction is towards
unified progression.
And it can only be achieved through—
love, equality, and respect.

Dark Side of The Moon

by Aru Deep

My teardrops shatter into sharp shards of emotion
Ricocheting off your indifferent titanium shield
Of ignorance
How are you so calm when our lives hang in the balance?
Perhaps yours don't, is that why?
What if they come for you too?

The veneer of biology separates us
Why do you feel so fortunate?
Your cornucopia is hollow
It is I who has more melanin, more oestrogen
What logic tipped the balance against us?

Lines have been drawn
In the sand, for all to see
With ink borne of blood, and the stylus of society
This gilded cage, a mirage that draws on my soul

Yin and yang, black and white, man and woman
And all who lay within the circle of life
Stop destroying their houses in nonsensical strife
When you look back at the human equation
Find it listing just to this side of equality
Hang your heads in shame
Don't mourn us then; we will have lost

But we will have ascended
To the dark side of the moon
Never to look back
On the seesaw painted with red.

Sometimes Decency Doesn't exist In The Dictionary

by Uniliar

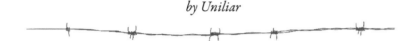

Take a walk with me down to the train stations, the carpark
and gaze into the windows of stores. Tell me, what do you see?

Hands sneaking through to the headlines of the news
uncovering the skin beneath our clothes, snaking down
the curves of our waist.
What was the point of having "stop" in our vocabulary when all they
do is defy it?
Laws that bound ropes upon our spine, choking our breaths and they
hope to grow unwanted flowers by planting seeds in our mouths.

Dresses and skirts, pants and shorts have a gender they say.
Do you remember being taught how to sit like a lady?
How to force the tears backwards as a boy?
Obliged to stare at a mirror for hours trying
to clone society's expectations into the tissues of our soul.
The taboos of kissing our lover of the same gender, different colour
as it isn't "normal".
Because we all must fit within the frame
of a perfect portrait that evils have painted.
Or be kicked out of existence,
into the shallows of disappointment and fear.

On the platform in broad daylight where the colour of their skin
bruised the same blue and purple, hair threatened the insecurities
of status and power and we're forced to degrade ourselves.
We can barely eat without being discriminated by the "smells"
of our food, our culture. Something we need to survive.
Pushed beyond the boundaries of being human, playing puppets and
dress ups.
Claiming our traditions as their new trend, bulleting
our voices onto platform nine and three quarters.
Sending us back into the greys of a forgotten bloodbath because of
uneducated infamy.

Society has been a child, constantly beckoning for more,
otherwise we feel the wrath of its tantrum and throws us aside.
It's time for it to grow up, to realise what is wrong, what is right
so, the next time we take a walk, we can enjoy the peace in the world
and not the pieces.

No Tolerance

by s.h.

The world is changing
The dreams don't matter
The sweet one you remember is no more
The reality is sinking
The truth is now standing
No more of hiding in the shadows
I will speak up and so should you.
I will not tolerate the lies told through
I am a queen, and I will protect my empire
No tolerance for the racist comments
Because the colour of my skin is not a threat
No tolerance for discrimination
Because the God made us equal
No tolerance for your nasty mind
Because my flesh is not your feast
No tolerance for homophobia
Because love is love and it always will be
Your privilege is not an excuse
It is a platform for you to speak up through
The world is not perfect, and neither are we
But we can work and right the wrongs of yesterday
Because for the mistakes my ancestors made
I shouldn't pay.

I Am Tired

by Madhurya Kommuri

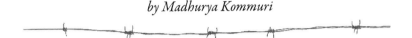

Strongest warriors have the toughest battles they say, trying to offer
some comfort,
But, what if that badge of honour does not outshine the hurt?

What if I am too tired to take this any forward,
What if I have more than enough suffered,
And can no longer hold on to my record?

What if I am done keeping my voice covered,
What if my future does seem to be a desert,
And I have enough lessons from life learnt?

What if so much injustice life did offer,
That things are all blurry and unclear,
And I can no longer handle it like a master?

What if I am tired of always being alert,
What if those words seem to me absurd,
And no longer as a warrior do I wish to be referred?

What if I am too tired to keep my mind diverted,
What if to a vulnerable child I wish to be reverted,
And to be that strong warrior I no more covet?

What if life's truth I have already uncovered,
But, from the wounds I will never recover?

I know I sound like a lost coward,
With no spirit and my head lowered,
But what if I really am exhausted and tired?

Unfolded Human Battle

by Divya Bora

Humans are surviving this battle since a long time,
Moving through the giant ancient doors to modern day closets,
Humans are fighting the battles from gender inequality to racism,
From colour discrimination to religious battles,

Crying, pleading, surviving through death from hunger,
A girl fighting to survive her pride being snatched,
A child waiting for the education s/he deserves,

This fight isn't getting over, no!
This change will cost a fight, worthy of the ones who can survive the
scars of brutality! Fight!

Fight such that it fills an empty stomach of the homeless on the roads
of poverty,
Fight for those questioning their identity based on their colour,

Fight rightfully for the change you want to bring,
Fight rightfully to bring peace within every soul,

Fight! Fight to remind them that every voice matters.
Fight.

Unfair Fight

by Noela Paraschiv

I am crawling on my knees,
yet I would never agree to give in,
to stand still.
A source that emanates strength,
I exist,
so therefore, I must fight until
I no longer have a beating heart,
or love to give
to the people that threw mud
at the one who fought for peace.

Is This The Land I Love

by Arti Chopra

The land that I love has shamed me,
The evil and the bestiality has maimed me,
The men of this valiant land have failed me,
Is this the country that I love?

Woman, who gives birth to you,
You have raped her and left her for dead,
Woman, who stands by you,
You violated her
wherever your devilish rage has led,
Woman who is worshipped and veneered as a deity
Resisted feebly, but made you see red,
Man became an animal preying on human flesh;
Is this the country I love?

Every day a rape, a harassment, an outrage of modesty
Safety of women in this land has become a travesty,
Respect for women, a thing of antiquity,
Is this the country I love?

She the nurturer, the mother, or the sister
Asks for your love, your respect, and your care
what is her fault in this?
that God made her a woman, pretty and fair?
Where is the chivalry, the nurture, and the protector?

That she looks for in you?
Who will be the guardian, the saviour?
Who will give her due? When will it happen?
That women feel loved respected and safe?
When will the indifference vanish?
When will the insensitivity stop to chafe?
When will men guard, respect and cherish women?
When will we ever feel safe?
Is this the country of valiant men?
Is this the country I love?

I Am A Woman

by Marissa Kovalenko

This is my world, come take a peek,
I'm viewed as weak,
Expected in all situations to act meek,
Be silent, don't speak, overtly critiqued,
I'm defined by my physique,
Every. Day. Of. The. Week,

I am a woman.

Step into my life, you might think twice,
I'm stronger than you understand,
After all, are children birthed by man?
And it may come as a surprise to you,
But I experience all the same emotions you do,
My brain works the same, as every one's does,
and thus, I have opinions and thoughts, and this is offensive because?

No man will ever experience the pressure,
Of their looks and body measuring up to ever-changing measures,
Their minds won't be questioned when they're spoken out loud,
and how is this acceptable in our world now?

I am proud,
I am strong,
I am intelligent,

I am capable,
I am more than enough.
I am not 'just a girl',
I AM A WOMAN.

Clarion Me

by Aparna Goswami

You say we don't let ourselves out
But, when we do, you judge us throughout.

Now it has been too long behind bars
A long time of hidden scars.
So today, let me come clean to you.
Yes, my mind is a little messed up
But that doesn't make me less assertive or capable.
Yes, there are days when every inch of my soul screams into the night.
When ghosts of mine conquer all
I still stand strong pretty tight.
Yes, I am afraid and sometimes obscure
and I don't always know what is the cure.
I am prone to anxiety and have been depressed
and if you call that mental, I will correct your illness.
Yes, I fall down but I am proud as I always stand back up
You will still judge me but guess what I don't give two bucks.

So, this is me abridged, straight and buckled up.
Come, I will take you on a ride to the path less known
And I'll be your girl in sweatshirts, a capstone.
Your girl, a little afraid but not frail anymore.
A world full of courage and will of stone.
My own self-love, my conditions upon.
I'll be outside this world full of scorn

Waiting for brothers who want peace and sisters seeking equality.
For sapiens looking for love and acceptance.
Come meet me there under that grove,
Where six colours of the sky do nothing unjust.
Where you don't have to give in to the prominent thrust
Till that day I'll wait here and stay
Having the chaos in me,

I'll still slay.

Speak Up

by Avi Baidya & Sharron Green

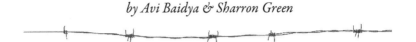

Speak up, speak out, and join the throng!
Now, as ever, challenge wrong.
Recognise not all are free
despite laws of equality.
Those not black have just not felt
the weaker hand they're often dealt.
Discrimination is no stranger,
environments more prone to danger.

Racism's not just black and white -
every colour must unite
against prejudice - it's not the norm
a newborn baby has no form -
it knows not what hue its skin will go.
What counts is that red blood flows
through everybody, heart & mind -
Mankind must leave racism behind.

That's why we should stand together,
abolish racism forever.
Privilege has to be checked,
Black lives deserve more respect.

Being A Girl

by Swati Thapa

She looked up wistfully at the pearly moon,
Wondering whether her life choices are a bane or a hidden boon.
Comparing in her mind the beauty of the moon and its dark shades,
To the charm of life and the many evils that she has faced.
The struggles, the conflicts in search of her identity,
The fights, the reunions solved with sanity.
Her hard work, her goals, and failures that she met,
Moments that made her feel proud of herself.
The many roles that she played beautifully,
The dark alleys, crossroads, and threats that she faced bravely.
Jeering of roadside loafers that made her feel uncomfortable,
Quickening of her pace to protect herself from being vulnerable.
Colleagues looking up to her at work for her ethics with admiration,
The unfriendly stares of unknown men peering into her soul as if in
damnation.
Making herself and her parents proud with her achievements,
But walking the streets with fear embedded in her heart,
Being cautious of people with bad intentions.
Raising her voice in this two-faced society which endorses
modernisation,
Where her cry is muffled in the name of a girl's limitations.
Questions often raised on her morals and upbringing,
Based on actions that were never her doing.
The society condemning and casting her away,
For trying to achieve her goals, her dreams in her own way.

Labelling her happiness on her relationship status,
Preventing her to reach for that inner peace of which she is desirous.
Despite these many hindrances and objections,
She marches on with no fear of perfection.
Keeping close the ones she loves the most as she aims for her goals
with no fear of rejection.
Raising her head up high each day keeping her fear aside,
Looking up to the moon, which is as beautiful as her,
but has its own dark side.

I'm A Girl

by Jacqueline Olivia

Look at me, I'm a girl.
I wear dresses, sit straight, and cross my legs
I play girly video games
I play tennis, volleyball, softball
I have opinions on celebrity news
I have knowledge in fashion
I know how to apply makeup
I can cook, wash dishes, do laundry
I can build a shed, mow a lawn, take out the trash
I know how to change a tire
I have knowledge in the stock market
I have opinions on politics
I play football, soccer, baseball
I play gory video games
I wear boxers and slouch with my legs open
Look at me, I'm a girl.

Facing The Voices

by Tanisha Thalnerkar

The voices in my head started echoing.
They chase me everywhere,
knocking down every door
that I shut in their faces.

They seem to always know my next step
even though we play this game of hide and seek
in a place full of mazes.

This place (my mind) became so hollow,
giving home to new demons
that lurk behind creaking doors.
They vocalise on those voices,
giving them new faces,
that laugh in mine,
mocking my pain, my helplessness, and my existence.

So, I started building a ladder
out of the words thrown at me
that once used to break me.
As I climb step by step
I hear the silence of the voices,
and I gaze at the absence of the demonic faces.

Bracing myself, I'm here now
at my newest peak,
where when I scream,
I only hear the voice
of my victory.

Rise

by Alexis Romo

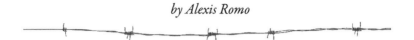

Revolution begins at the call of the strong, so let us
Incite the call to bring forth our revolutionaries and our warriors.
Speak now, loudly, and scream at the top of your lungs -
Eventually, peace will win.
We will win.

STORIES

1

JUSTICE

by Snehal Agarwal

I gulped. My sweaty palms were proof that my mind was still contemplating on whether to enter the pale-yellow building, in front of which my weak legs had halted. They refused to move forward. 'Police Station', the years old sign board dangling on the top of the building, read. My trembling lips hesitated to recount the nightmares of last night. My eyes were exhausted from the endless tears and were helplessly looking around, begging for justice.

"I need to do this." I repeated to myself.

"That monster should be punished for his barbaric acts." I closed my eyes, reiterating this, to muster all my energy to step inside the police station and file my case. However, glimpses of the horrifying events flashed my mind. I succumbed into the darkness again.

"A tyre puncture?" he had asked. with a voice laced with genuine concern as he rolled down the windows of his car. The sun had bid adieu when I was leaving from work and it was a starless night. Pushing my scooter along the roadside alone with a dead mobile phone, the voice of help was a relief to my ears, and I replied with urgency, "Yes, please, help me."

My eyes were gleaming with hope as this less travelled road had infrequent visitors and here was the first and last one offering assistance.

"Leave your scooty at the roadside and come in, I'll drop you home and you can come back with aid in the morning to get your scooty." he suggested calmly. Having no other option, I pulled out my stuff from the trunk of the scooty and got into the car, thanking him profusely. If only I knew this act of kindness was in fact a hoax...

The long, dark road to the town ensured that we couldn't speed up. Numerous thoughts bothered me, and I wished that I had charged my phone at work so that I could inform my family about my situation. Seeing me all worked up, he cooed, "It's okay, you are safe now." Soothed by his kind words, I sighed.

Minutes passed and we were driving up the lonely road, my eyes strained to look outside the window. Suddenly, I felt a brush on my knee. I turned to look at him immediately and saw his hand on the gear. I shrugged, believing that it was a mistake while changing the gears. Oh, why was I so gullible?

Soon, there was another brush and my body numbed as this did not feel like a harmless mistake. The next brush was a little higher than my knees and I moved in my seat uncomfortably. My eyes clouded with fear and suspicion as they searched for guilt in his eyes. No guilt found. Just lust. My heart was pounding in my chest so loud that I'm sure it was audible over the silence of the eerie night.

His lips curled up in amusement on seeing my reaction and then he placed his palm on my thigh. I shrieked and swatted his hand away as he pressed the brakes of the car with a jolt.

"You are feisty!" he exclaimed as he central locked the doors of the car and placed another palm on my mouth tightly. I moved my hands, pushing the man away, realising how well-built he was as he moved up from his seat and tried to overpower me. I kicked, moved and jumped, and bit his hand but all in vain as his huge frame pinned me down.

The passenger seat was adjusted quickly by him as he pushed me down with his weight. Nasty tears flowed down my cheeks and my bloody screams were muffled. He stared at me briefly, before gagging me with a cloth and beginning to exploit me. I was immobilized as he abused me in all ways, feeling so powerless.

A loud horn of a police van entering the premises brought me back to the present before I re-lived the scenes where the vicious man had taken away my virtue. Eager to see my assaulter punished, I finally made my way inside the building. My tongue moistened my lips as I prepared to narrate the details of the attack and how I was left on the roadside after I felt unconscious from the unbearable pain inflicted on my body. How I was left on display with just a blanket of shame and self-hatred covering me. How I felt empty of emotions and void of soul after my body was played with.

"I want to file a FIR against a man who raped me last night." I announced on meeting the first person in uniform after entering the police station. My voice was filled with eagerness and a subtle hint of pain.

"This way please," he showed me the way emphatically to the right table. Nodding my head, I moved towards it before I saw the man behind the desk.

My legs froze and it felt as if someone punched the wind out of my lungs. My whole world was spinning, and my body turned into jelly. The sight of the man who broke me into a million pieces, who damaged me and left me to die was sitting in a khaki suit with a polished name tag referring to him as an Inspector. With the FIR register in his hands, he seemed unaffected by the crime he committed last night.

"Who is going to file my complaint now?" I murmured, unable to process my next move.

My abuser was supposed to be my protector.

A police inspector had raped me.

2

NOT ALL MONSTERS ARE UNDER YOUR BED

by Omaira Mahan

Winter. I start heading back from home from the gas station, where I often go to get my favourite soda and hot chips. You start following me from behind. I can hear you getting closer. I walk faster so you don't stop me, for I have to be at home before dark. You snuck up right next to me and turn on your siren. I stop.

Startled. You step out of your car and ask me where I am going. Home. Where else? You tell me to remove my hood. A breeze suddenly hit, rushing chills down my spine. I stand there, shaking, attempting to walk in place so I don't feel the cold. You tell me not to move. I ask you why I am being stopped-for my mother was going to worry if I didn't get home in time. You keep asking me where I'm going, and I repeatedly tell you that I'm going home. You don't listen. You ask again and I respond-again. Your voice becomes aggressive and so does mine. My chips start moving in my pocket. I grab them and you pull out your gun. My bag of chips fell to the ground.

Numb. I instantly put my hands up. Please don't shoot. I was only reaching for my chips, so they don't get crushed. I don't like when they get crushed. Am I a threat to you?

You tell me to get on the ground and I beg for you not to shoot because I had to get home to my mother, and I had done absolutely nothing wrong.

You yell at me and tell me to remain on the ground with my hands up. Terrified. Tears start streaming down my face. I don't know what to do.

My phone. It is sitting in the left pocket of my jeans. "I want to call my mother." I tell you as I reach into my pocket.

"Stop!" You scream. "Don't grab it!"

Confused.

"I have to call my-"

Your hand tightens on your gun as you step farther from me.

Am I really the one in fear, or are you?

I continue to fight it.

"What's in your pocket?!" You yell.

"I want to take my phone out to call-", I desperately try to explain to you, but you wouldn't listen.

I finally reach into my pocket. Bang.

My body feels hot, as I fall to the ground. Bang. Another one.

You shot me twice in my leg. My soda, chips and phone all fell out. I lay there. The room spinning, my body feeling hot. Excruciating pain.

I was always taught that the most terrifying monsters live under your bed, or in your closet. That they have claws, and 4 eyes with a long tongue and sharp teeth and will most certainly kill you.

They were wrong.

The most terrifying monsters do not look terrifying at all. They don't live under your bed or in the closet.

In fact, the most terrifying monsters wear a police uniform. They drive a police car. They are disguised as heroes- but are the darkest villains of them all.

And they will *Kill* you.

3

THE GREAT REBELLION

by Shaymi Shah

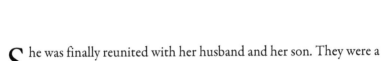

S he was finally reunited with her husband and her son. They were a very different kind of family- they would travel to different places all year and only at certain times would their routes converge into a common destination; that's when they would all meet. They had all divided their duties amongst each other.

Her work, she believed was to make sure everything she has under her control, is in order. So, she would keep regular checks on her employees and take progress reports from them from time to time. But she never felt satisfied enough, so she would even revisit the same places sometimes herself. She wasn't someone who would take no for an answer easily or would let anyone take her for granted. She was someone who would always ask for a justification, hear them out, and then make a rightful decision. She was indeed a good listener. She would forgive but only after making sure there was a lesson learned from the mistake they had made.

She could flawlessly disguise herself into different forms while visiting places all year, meeting different people of all ages, genders, castes, and classes.

Sometimes, the residents of the cities would organize huge concerts for announcing her arrival and sometimes they would all gather for a huge dance party. Sometimes she would be requested to give a speech while sometimes they would meet up with her alone and tell her about their problems of which they sought solutions. Most of the residents considered her to be "the ideal woman" and hence, they all had a picture of her or a sculpture that looked like her in their homes.

Most of her speeches were inspiring stories about her life, her fights, her rebellions, and the experiences that made her such a strong woman. She had played several roles of a mother, a daughter, a wife, and most of all an independent powerful woman- all her life.

She would tell not just women but all the residents how important it was to respect each other, spread love, and celebrate life. They would all eagerly listen to her stories, feel happy while listening to her achievements, and be inspired to be like her. But they would often make the same mistake once she left.

The men wouldn't stop abusing their wives, raping girls, or torturing their daughters. They would objectify them and harass them all the time. The men thought it was normal to do this, and that it was only powerful women like her, who had achieved so much in their lives, that needed to be respected, others were mere objects that they could play with and throw away once they got bored of them. Even the women who had been so mesmerized by her presence and inspired by her stories would once again go back to succumbing to the wishes of the men they lived with- they would helplessly endure the pain and torture that they now had started believing they deserved.

That day was one such day when she visited the city where she and her family always planned to meet every year before they parted ways again. Her son always believed that he had to be there to welcome his parents, so he would always reach earlier than they did. Her husband was a true lover, a great listener, and a keen observer. Rather than speaking about his travels, he would always ask her to narrate her experiences first.

She told them how she felt so mesmerized by that place. She seemed quite amazed as to how even people who didn't know her, found her so familiar. The hospitality and the kindness of the residents were truly remarkable. To this, her son told her that he had found out how she had become so famous over time as her stories were passed on to generations by now. They were all talking about the city that night and analysing the progress the people had made here since last year. It seemed that in comparison to the several cities they had travelled to, this particular one had hardly changed. The reports said that the men still dominated women by the exact percentage they did five years ago, and they had even taught their sons to do the same to their daughters-in-law by now. They were all very adamant about breaking the legacy their forefathers had created years ago. They were so bound by their pride and honour that they never even thought of changing their perceptions towards living in a certain way, with time. It saddened the three of them to think that no matter how much they had tried, this particular family remained the same.

They were all thinking of ideas of what they could do to try and bring some change in the belief system and values of this family.

To this, she told her son and her husband that she was going to get a speech ready by the next morning itself and say it out loud to them. If they were still hesitant to do what she asked, she will find a way to teach them a lesson.

In the morning, the residents gathered around her as usual, greeted her, and offered her breakfast. She asked the women to leave and asked the men to stay back.

She told them to sit around her as she had something to say to them. As soon as they all settled, she began talking. She said, "First of all, I have to thank you all for welcoming me so dearly. I wasn't sure if you all knew me well, and you still gave me so much respect and love. But I have to tell you all about something I have noticed. As you all know, my family and I travel all year, to different cities, and look after our business. I am in charge of making sure that there is constant progress in the perceptions of the residents of all these cities and their behaviour towards each other; especially women. But I heard of some very peculiar observations from my employees and I must say it has made me rather unhappy. I have heard that once I leave, you all get back to being the same people- you show no change whatsoever in the way you behave with the women around you. You don't even try. You remain the same egoistic, self-loathing men you have always been. You abuse your wives, mistreat your daughters, and harass your daughters-in-law just the same. May I ask why do you feel the need to do so? You have heard so many stories about me, you even get inspired to become better, and the moment I turn to leave, you give up on becoming better and just do what you've always done? Will you please tell me what makes you surrender to your inner instincts of becoming so evil? Yes! Evil is the word I have for you all, that's how furious I am. It's been over five years and your reports show not one percent progress? You are all such cowards, disastrous human beings, who live only to please themselves. All this pride and honour you talk about, are you going to take it to the grave with you? Do you realize you might just live a little longer and remain healthier if you treat and respect the women you live with, in a good way, as it will at least help them cook good food for you and serve you well?

You have already crushed their confidence and stolen their individuality, why are you still taking their remaining life away from them? Are you not ashamed of yourselves?

You do so many things for me when I come to visit you every year, but what about those who stay with you all your life? Do they not deserve respect too?

You buy so many jewels and clothes for me, knowing that I am not even going to take them with me, as I don't really need them. If that's your way to shower love for me, why don't you buy it for those who matter?

You prepare huge feasts and celebrate my arrival so dearly, but what about the women who prepare food for you lifelong, is it so hard to take them out once in a while and celebrate your life with them?

You show me how much you love me by spending so much time with me, every morning when you wake up and every evening before dinner, can't you show some of that love to the women who without any confrontation choose to love you forever?

You give me so much respect and attention, you listen to me carefully, fulfil my wishes, but when it comes to doing the same thing for the women who promised to stand by you, it becomes such a difficult thing to do, doesn't it?

Pay attention as what I am about to say is very important, you are all wrong to think that I visit you all because I am fond of you. The truth is, I come here to check on you, to see if your wives and daughters look happier than before. You have all misinterpreted my presence and thought it was for you when in reality it was for them - the ones who believed not merely in me but themselves enough - to think that someday even they will get the deserved respect and attention that they craved for all their lives. It was for the women who have heard all my stories and are willing to make those stories their own.

It was for the women who may have given up on changing cold-hearted men like you but still choose to love you no matter what. It was for the women who stand by you even if you make sure they aren't even able to walk half the time due to the blows they receive from you all.

I am so disappointed in all of you. But I am not someone you can take for granted, believe me. I am going to leave a day earlier this year and give you time to contemplate your actions. I will come back next year to check on you again, and if I still don't see any progress, you better get ready to witness something you couldn't even imagine can happen to you."

She finally took a breath and stopped talking. She saw tears in the eyes of the men who were sitting around her. They all seemed to be spellbound. One of them opened the doors of the room they were in and asked the women to come in.

She was surprised to see that when the women entered the room, the men stood in front of them with their hands as if in prayer, asking for forgiveness and their heads down.

The Devi finally smiled at them and blessed them. She told them how this was merely a step closer to achieving the end goal and now they also were a part of the biggest rebellion she had ever started in order to bring a revolutionary change in the human world.

4

FOR A NICKEL

by Tiffany Lindfield

Annie stood at a booth at the big fair in Jackson, Tennessee. She felt out of place, like weeds seeping from the cracks of a paved road. She felt this way every time she left the farm—her land, and the farmhouse sitting on it. A place where she would lay on the porch swing, half-awake, watching the sun show off through Purple Fountain grass she let run wild.

Earlier, she had people watched, as her husband had made small talk with the other men, other men watching over their wives at booths--before he tired and went home. She had watched with curiosity and even joy, but after the hours piled on top of the other, dragging the sun to the ground, those pleasant emotions had faded to contempt; annoyance at the faces, the bags of cotton candy, the screams, the sticky relish on hot dogs, children skipping, parents wiping brows, smiles wide, and eyes twinkling at the assortment of attractions.

Patty, the chicken—the reason her husband had Annie standing at the booth so long her feet ached—had stopped clucking for home. Instead Patty sat, resigned—it was too hot to make a fuss—on legs so stout they looked like the barrel post holding the farm's mailbox up.

A woman walked up with a tall man and a little boy with freckles around his button-down nose, and Annie tried to force a smile, but it was no use. Her lips twitched instead, "A nickel to give her a look over."

The tall man tipped his hat to the sign above Annie's head: **FREAKISH HEN**

Annie lifted the crate holding Patty, custom built by her husband, to the booth's tabletop. She opened the door, but Patty was done for the day and sat still. Annie fished a pellet from her pocket. "Come on now, girl. *Tith, tith, tith, tith.* Come on."

"Well is she gonna come out? I ain't paying unless she comes out and we can give her a good look-over ma'am. That's only fair."

The man's wife smiled, as if to agree. The little boy had one of his fingers poked in the crate, "I want to see you! Get out!"

Annie gulped. None of it seemed right to her. Patty being called a freak; She was big. The biggest hen Annie had ever seen, most folks had ever seen. She towered every rooster and here she sat being poked by some city-folk's brat, made to do this and that for nickels.

Annie slapped the kid's hand away. "Stop that, now!"

The boy puckered his lip, tuckering under his mom's arm. "You're a mean lady."

"Is this how you treat your customers?" the father asked.

Annie didn't hear them. She was closing the crate door and packing up. Patty clucked again, in the know. Annie did not hear Mr. Matthews hollering behind her, either. With his face beet red, he asked her what she was doing, and where did-she-think-she was going, huffing he would tell her husband all about her.

"Damned Injun blood," Mr. Matthews said under his breath, and Annie turned around, hearing that; her mouth snarled like a dog ready to bite, but she didn't make a sound, other than her teeth clicking together. She stomped past the flea circus, which she learned involved gluing the bug's tiny legs to tiny objects, then the peep show, and on her face wore the continued expression of disgust.

Three Years and Some Months Later

Annie was a baby the first time she had seen a chicken give itself a dust bath. But she doesn't remember being a baby or what she saw. Just using *deduction.* That's a word her younger sister who ran off to Birmingham with a high-time lawyer uses—a man twenty years her senior. Annie's sister wears fine jewelry now, talks fine, and matches her shoes to her coat, to her handbag. Annie's sister says she has to please him at least once a week or so to keep herself suited without his complaining about how much such a thing costs. "That's the nice way of saying you let him fuck you," Annie had told her, feeling lucky enough to be widowed; Horse had kicked her husband Bob to death three years ago—lest' that's what the papers *said*.

Annie was out in the yard, tending to her cabbage patch when Patty started in for a dust bath. No matter how many times she had seen it, she had to stop, and watch. She knew that if a thing were pleasant enough, you didn't tire of it. And if you did, it didn't matter. She knew contentment seesawed with complacency just fine, not requiring military attention.

Annie watched Patty kick up the next dust bowl when a stick-legged woman with red hair trekked up her drive. A two-mile dirt road. The woman had a basket in her hand, and Annie thought she must be trying to sell her something. Like the insurance salesman three years ago who had talked her husband into a life insurance policy.

The woman couldn't see Annie on the down slope, but Annie saw the woman using her hands as a shield against a lazy August sun. Annie tossed her hat back on her head, more grateful for the hat now, seeing someone without one. Annie didn't wave or anything, stood there, waiting on the woman to spot her. Like a hawk looking for one of Patty's baby chicks hiding under a blanket of sweet Alyssum. Their yellow heads resembling sprouts of corn in the blooms of pink and baby blue.

On the uphill, the woman spotted Annie, and waved, but Annie didn't make a show of anything. Just waited for the stranger to near.

The woman, out of breath, stood at the bottom of the porch. "Howdy, Miss. How are you?"

"Reckon, I'm well. You want some tea?"

Sweat and humidity had made the woman's dress stick to her body like tape. "That would be divine. My name is Marla"

"Divine," Annie chuckled. "I'm Annie. Folks who like me call me that. Folks who don't, clip it to Ann. Take a seat now. I'll go get us a pitcher of tea."

Annie pulled a tall glass pitcher of tea from the icebox, chipped some ice in a bucket, grabbed a few oranges, and went to grab glasses from the cupboard when the woman peered in the doorway like a squirrel. "You need any help?"

"You can help carry."

Annie took in the young woman's bright red hair and the freckles on her cheeks that seemed to glitter. Annie turned her glass up, greedy, some tea dripping down her chin. Dirt from the garden was on her cheeks, and chicken poop on the bottom of her shoeless feet. The woman's cheeks were pink with blush, and she sipped the tea daintily.

Annie began to roll a cigarette. "Tea good?"

"It is perfectly sweet," Marla responded.

"I don't do any of that Jesus stuff." Annie blurted out.

"I'm sorry?"

"I don't serve anyone who's a man or who is white. I'm a Choctaw woman. My mother was stolen from her tribe. I am her daughter." Annie said proudly, tilting her chin to show off jet black hair, black eyes wrapped in wrinkles, and chiseled cheekbones.

"I am not here to sell the gospel—but books."

"Books about what?"

"I write stories. Short stories. You fancy, Mark Twain?"

"Who?"

"He's a famous writer."

"Never heard of 'em."

Marla's eyes darted, raising her basket onto knobby knees. The basket had two flaps, and she opened one side, pulling a small book out. Other books were in the basket. Marla carefully laid the book on the metal table. Annie picked it up, blowing smoke from her cigarette. There was a small farmhouse on the cover that looked a lot like Annie's house, but she couldn't make out the writing on the cover. Annie flipped through it, then placed her nose in its center, taking in a big whiff, like she did the flowers and herbs of the yard.

"You walked all this way to sell me a story?"

The little woman looked down. "I want to be famous like Mark Twain. Make my own way, somehow."

"You write this?"

"Yes, ma'am."

"Then you're a writer. How much do they go for? These books you got?"

Marla opened the basket and pulled three more out of the basket.

"All the same?" Annie asked, puzzled. "I never saw so many of the same book before. I don't think."

"A big new printer in Jackson, Mississippi printed me ten copies," the woman bragged.

"How much do you want me to pay for the books?"

Marla smiled, averting her gaze. "They are a quarter a piece."

Annie jumped up, nearly tripping as she ran in the house to her dresser drawer. She opened a small box, and inside lay hundreds of dollars from her husband's life insurance. She grabbed two bills and walked back outside to see the woman in near tears. Annie knew she had probably walked miles today and sold a copy at best. At worst, none. "Here."

Marla's mouth opened, and her eyes opened wider. "How many books do you want, ma'am?"

"I just need one, but you take that and get ya' some more books or paper or whatever you need to write.

"No. I cannot possibly take this. It would not be proper."

"You lookin' a gift horse in the mouth?" Annie asked

"No ma'am. No. It is just...I do not know what to say."

"What's to say about survival?

5

THE ROOMMATE

by Shakira Washington

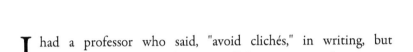

I had a professor who said, "avoid clichés," in writing, but unfortunately, it is the only way to tell this story correctly.

I arrived in the big city of Philadelphia from my humble Midwestern town on a steamy August afternoon. My mother and I packed the rental car with all my belongings, and we drove for over twelve hours. I contorted my body to fit in the car around the bins and boxes. When we arrived, my mom and I unloaded the car, while everyone else's entire families helped. It was the first difference I noticed, but I tried not to let it discourage me. My mom cried as she drove off, but I was fearless. I was a small fish in a big pond, and everyone knew that except me.

I had grand expectations of the East Coast. Growing up in the Bible Belt, I experienced casual racism to the point that it almost seemed normal. I assumed going to a big city people were more open and tolerant. I consciously decided to go to college far from home to pursue my dream of working in fashion and escape that small-town mentality. I learned a hard lesson, though. Predominately white spaces perpetuated the same bigotry, liberal or conservative, it did not matter. Racism in the Midwest wore Carhartt boots and Dickies overalls, while in the Northeast, it wore North Face jackets and Uggs.

I tried to make friends. However, my endless friendliness, highly valued in Indiana, was not welcomed in Philadelphia. Many people could not overlook that my family was from the south and, therefore, I was a descendant of slaves (I guess that's not interesting enough). My constant use of the phrase y'all made me stick out like a sore thumb and garnered me continuous ridicule. I was desperate to make some friends, and I thought I found one in my roommate, but all that glitters isn't gold.

The honeymoon phase ended a couple of weeks into my first semester. My roommate said to me, "When I heard I was getting a black roommate, I was excited, but now I'm disappointed." She spoke like someone unsatisfied that her pistachio ice cream tasted like green food coloured vanilla. "I thought you were going to be like those black girls on TV—loud, funny, ghetto. You're like a regular person. It's boring." She swung her long brunette hair and put a hand on her hip and gestured stereotypical ethnic movements.

The next red flag occurred when I came home from class one day, and my roommate's tall, athletic frame stood in the middle of the room with a broom. She shouted, "You need to sweep your side of the room. I swept our sides (we had a 3rd roommate, another white girl). Our hair is straight, and your hair is squiggly. And I'm not sweeping up squiggly hair!" She scolded me like a mother walking into a messy bedroom that I should have cleaned already.

Strike three, happened on Sunday afternoon when we were watching TV. My roommate leaned over and touched my hair and commented. "One day, when you're sleeping, I will cut your hair and see if it grows back, like a chia pet!" I countered, "You cut my hair; I'll slit your throat." (Remember this, it will get me in trouble later.) I quickly snapped back like a Black woman who did not take "jokes" lightly about her hair.

Now, the question I often get asked is, "why didn't I get out right then and there?" Remember, I was far from home in a new city, and I was trying to make friends. I was the lone chocolate chip in the cookie dough, so I was already walking a fine line. I came from a state most people did not realize existed. I complained daily about what passed for fried chicken, and I was a proud Colts fan, not Eagles. Not to mention, this was the late 2000's, the term thick had not entered the mainstream lexicon, and my big bum, muscular thighs, and voluminous breasts took up space. My classmates always reminded me that I needed to make myself smaller and quieter.

I did not have the vocabulary then, but these constant microaggressions were slowly wearing me down. I promised myself I would stay composed and not lose my temper. However, on an October night, right before she went to bed, my roommate said, "Your mom is not pulling her weight. Our parents are here every weekend buying snacks, cleaning, and doing laundry. Where is your mom?" Annoyed, I replied, "She is in Indiana, that's like 800 miles away." My roommate retorted, "Well, that's not my problem. You chose to go to college far from home. So, you need to figure it out!" She laid down and flipped over, so her back was facing me. Filled with anger, I turned off the light before walking out.

My roommate alluded to this before. I never asked for help, and I was used to the digs about being raised by a single mother. I ignored her comments mostly, but on this day, I had had enough. I went out to get some air, thinking the cool autumn breeze would soothe me like a baby needing a pacifier. However, I walked back into my dorm room and slammed the door. You can talk about my hair, what I eat, and what I like to watch on TV, but you can't talk about my Mama. That's the straw that broke the camel's back.

What happened after this is a blur like I blacked out in rage. I was the angry black woman now, and I was not backing down. My roommate shrieked in surprise and jumped out of her loft bed. We stood toe to toe, both of us screaming. At 5'11, she could have easily squashed my 5'2 frame, but I swear I saw her shrink before my eyes. This was not the best way to handle the situation, but hindsight is always 20/20.

Our argument woke up the entire floor as it was after midnight. I was so out of sorts that my roommate was scared to be near me. The school banned me from my room, and I spent the next few nights sleeping on a classmate's cold dorm floor. The punishment from the university was swift, and the aftermath was brutal. In short, despite my retelling of being bullied, the fact I threatened to slit her throat was thrown back in my face. They forced me to move out of my room and find new roommates.

The entire process, from meeting with counsellors to finding new roommates and moving from the basement to the third floor, happened in two weeks. They also banned me from returning to the basement, but they did not need to tell me twice. Mark my words, I was never going back. From that point on, I was no longer the friendly black girl from the state no one could remember. I was like a supervillain, the mad black woman, the most terrifying of them all.

My other problem, I had to new find roommates within two weeks, or the school threatened to kick me off-campus. I was up a creek without a paddle, as my grandma would say. Finding new roommates was like speed dating. I scheduled dates to meet the scorned roommate and my potential new living partners. All parties needed to agree, and not too many were keen on the crazy black girl. I also needed to find someone to help me move. It was a daunting task between keeping up with my design work. Not to mention the university was unsympathetic and unhelpful.

However, suddenly, I received a call to meet a potential new roommate at 11 pm. We met hastily, did some shady backroom deal, and I was out of there the next day. The school even broke protocol to have all the male Resident Assistants help me move up three flights in my all-girl dorm. The tone switched from apathetic to concerned, but I did not care. I was relieved that I was not expelled from college and homeless.

At the end of my freshman year, I received a formal apology from the university. My old roommate bullied other girls (shocking, I know), and they released her from the field hockey team. I never saw her again. That's the way the cookie crumbles, I guess. It was not until after I graduated, that I found out my mom called the university and gave them a sermon about how they would and would not treat her daughter. Suddenly, the actions of those two weeks made sense. When I asked my mom why she called the university and why she did not tell me about it, she replied in her motherly tone. "You've always been able to handle your problems, and I only step in when I need to. I may be 800 miles away, but nobody messes with my baby."

6

WE ARE THE FAKE LORDS OF OUR IMAGINATIVE FIEFDOMS

by Usama bin Tanveer

The word fiefdom ferries me back to the terrains under Pharaoh's rule. It is said that the territory under his control stretched past the limits of today's imaginative minds. With the exception of stars and celestial objects, the Pharaoh had his territorial claims established roughly everywhere. It is this antediluvian preaching that makes me assume that the ancient Chinese proverb, "Everything under the sun belongs to God" (in this case their emperor, perhaps) is, probably, an inspiration from the Pharaoh's fiefdoms.

Unknowingly though, Pharaoh had embraced the reality that there was something -of which he only knew and never rationally imagined - beyond his grip, thus validating an established reality: The Lord's authority begins where that devolved to the worldly lords ends.

Pharaoh, in his hubris, proclaimed himself God.

Unarguably, he was a fake Lord. The reality of his unreal Lordship was unleashed by comparatively meagre Musa(as).

Although in essence, Musa's position was firmer, while on the ground, Pharaoh's foothold was stronger.

Moving forward, when Musa(as) invoked the celestial phenomenon and challenged Pharaoh to intrude it, he was taken aback. If we look inquisitively, it probably wasn't Pharaoh's helplessness against the divinely regulated celestial phenomenon which laid the foundations of his reign's decline, but perhaps his pompous arrogance, drenched in the power of his controlled fiefdoms, which did so.

Such is the "power of power" that it incapacitates its bearer of any imaginative and rationally- aspired critical thinking, necessary for its sustenance. Had Pharaoh known the answers to Musa's challenge, he'd have better guarded his rule. But the power of power had blinded him of any imagination beyond his power.

I can have a phantasmagorical imagination of how an otherwise weak Musa(as), laced with divine logic, would be blushing upon sensing his triumph against the erroneously acclaimed lord, while he made him loose the battle of rational imagination.

Speaking of the contemporary times, it seems as we've gathered a major part of our inspiration from Mr. Pharaoh's behaviour. How? Let me show you.

A man half-naked (or half-dressed, whichever way one might see it) was lying in his bedroom and enjoying the dance of *Anjuman*, the dream girl of the '80s. During the course of his enjoyment, he heard the voices of his daughters and wife, arguing on some matter. He promptly muted the television's volume and upped his own. I must admit, he was well-versed with roughly all the abuses usually sounded in our society, and he made no secret of his abuse-uttering ability.

On being asked what triggered his anger, "The high pitch of women's voices echoing in the house and possibly crossing its walls," had he responded.

Then followed an oppressive lecture on the subject of Purdah[1]. And in doing so, he was unhinged to the extent that he openly mentioned almost all the physical parts of his daughters and wife, as well as their poses of sleep. Remember, I was a Na Mahram[2] sitting there in front of whom such uncensored content was being vomited out.

As the lecture grew uglier, the daughters, too, did not hesitate of my presence and hurled their unheard cries unto their father. Their primary grievances were:

a) He (father) never paid for their educational fees, despite earning a healthy income.

b) He was indifferent to the budget of the house.

c) He was impervious to their emotional needs.

d) He never took care of their dressing.

e) He always subjected them to undue suspicion.

f) He always publicly humiliated them.

g) He never took them in confidence while taking any decision and infringed upon their personal freedom.

h) He always disdainfully repudiated their mother.

i) He was apathetic to her needs.

j) For years, he took her pay and openly held that he was against her job.

k) He was insecurely obsessed with her.

l) He was always evasive of the financial matters of every sort and they triggered his fury.

Shockingly, the father didn't object to any of these grievances. He was, however, of the view that he believed in saving and investing money in property, only to be expended on his daughters' weddings and not much on their education.

On the other hand, the daughters endeavoured to make him realise that it was his unfair quest for unlimited power that had prompted them to stand against him. They also argued that since he was domestically at the helm of their affairs, he needed to manage this role, rather exploit it.

However, the hubris of his longed-for power had blinded his rational imaginative ability to the extent that anything other than his power was inaudible to him, as was the case with the Pharaoh. This establishes to me the very fact that rationality and critically conscious imaginative thinking have been and continue to be the undeniable tools to puncture the fake claims of Lordship. Also, should be kept in mind the fact that power is only the Almighty's discretion. What HE bequeaths upon people is "authority" and authority has to be managed, rather than confused with power and manipulatively exploited.

That is so because the Giver of the authority has a thousand avenues to take it back.

To conclude, I feel bad for the Pharaoh. He had actual fiefdoms under his governing belt, yet perished at the hands of God's aggression. However, today's Pharaohs even lack the sense of fiefdoms, let alone owning or governing them, yet continue to oppress their dependants unabated. The lesson for us is to neither get blinded by the "power of authority", nor frustrated by the tyranny of the oppressors. The rational imaginative ability has the soft power to overthrow thrones, and we need to strive for that.

***

[1]Purdah: Veil

[2]Na Mahram: An Adult

7

EASY MONEY

by Tiffany Lindfield

I lounge in fatigue with my cheek pressed against my grandmother's quilt, one sewn by her hand years ago. Even without a mirror, I know the imprint of one of her quilted roses sits on my cheek.

The buzzing of my faux diamond-studded phone is to blame. It's the weekend flow, after all; back to back clients. Someone looking for *Jasmine Ice*; me. I am Jasmine Ice. Clients like you better if you have a name that allows them to pair flowers with fucking, anything but a human being with a beating heart.

I feel like death, sitting up, topless, staring at my new breast with scars fresh and they are still sore. They weren't what I had expected, taunt and the left boob oddly shifted to the right. The surgeon has promised to fix that. I nudge the breast—as if it were just a thing and not a part of my body—to where it should be, but it quickly resumes its quirky position.

I wipe the make-up smeared on my face with the bedsheet, finally looking at my phone, hoping the one wrangling me was *easy money*. Not sure I can stomach another obese man, believing I may die if I must suck another limp cock while holding a roll of lard above my head. Just a nice old man; Many of them just want to prance us around like trinkets at silly corporate parties. Many of the old-timers too are old for sex, settling for stripteases--or dirty talk.

I turn on the bed lamp, letting a small glow of light cast across my newest book, 'Cunt,' which sits turned open, the sentence I highlighted, still, leaping from the page.

Once the rape scene is underway, stand up and scream. Freak. Loudly narrate your own version of what is happening on the screen: "Now she is pounding his face into the metal stairs of the fire escape. Her shoe is off. Ooo! Spiked HEEL to the temple..."

I look back to the phone, finally reading the message; SWM, twenty-five seeks a young female; he has attached a picture. Must be attractive, I think as I watch the image download. Pretty boys send pictures.

He was pretty, dressed well, and young. It's the young ones that scare me the most. Most of them cocky, trust fund brats with an insatiable appetite for rough anal. Thanks, Pornhub. It's as if they are unable to orgasm unless the smell of blood, sweat, and tears slap them across the face.

Then there were the rare few who were awkward, sweet, nervous—like small mice. I made the symbol of an eagle to the sky, attempting to summon the good graces of some She-God, "A mouse, God. A mouse," I pray, looking down to my vagina still swollen from the last guy.

I met the eyes of my tabby cat, telling him, "Don't judge me. You're always judging me."

He meows in some feline protest.

The ritual begins—Shower, make-up, something sexy, perfume, always making the effort to spread my legs, drenching my pussy in *Flowerbomb*. Men don't seem to want real pussy anymore, but some candied apple version of it. Thanks, Playboy. I have this secret desire that some man—if he actually takes the time to give me head—will find themselves poisoned with just the right amount of my cum and the chemical concoction (call it *cuntcoction*). I'm bitter. That's what the sex industry does to us; It chews us up and spits on our faces—literally.

I stand in the kitchen with my same ole' black dress and heels. The darkness of the room makes me feel pathetic, and I remember the ache inside me. It's still light outside and here I'm cramped in the dark like a vampire. I yawn, reaching for the chain above my head with a fairy figurine on the end. I grasp her porcelain legs, yanking, and light floods the room. Damn, I need to clean. Dishes are piled high. Is there anything to eat?

No, not much.

Opening the microwave, I pull out a T.V dinner from earlier that day, still uneaten. It will have to do. I poke at it. Tamale, rice, and beans.

Maybe not.

I pull a bottle of Sunny Up from the fridge instead. I'll add Vodka. I can't do any of this without numbing cream. I pull the Vodka from a top cabinet hearing the glass bottom scrape against cheap wood, mixing the drink with the orange liquid in a plastic cup. Squatting to the floor with another yawn, I turn the cup up. Liam slides past my legs, meowing again, this time, incessant.

"What? I ask but know he's hungry. I open a can of wet food, slapping the food straight from the can to the floor.

"Here," I say as he looks up, annoyed. "What, water, too?" Of course, water too, you idiot," I berate myself, picking up his small, steel bowl. "Ewwh," I say, washing slime from the sides with a smelly dish rag. I sit it back down, refilled with tap water; Liam seems happy.

Finally.

I can do this. I can keep a cat alive.

"I gotta go," I tell him, leaving my apartment. No need to lock the door. What's to take? I get in the car.

Finding my cell, I locate his world--it's a man's world—his address is a familiar place; an upscale hotel, leaving me to assume this one was wealthy or at least wanted to be. Most of my clients were rich or pretended to be. I guess you could call me a high-class hooker. Like Julia Roberts in *Pretty Woman, only not as pretty.*

I text him, and he seems cordial, seemingly innocent, as innocent as a John can be. He gives me the rundown on where to park, telling me to meet him in the front lobby. Buddy, my lookout will be there, too. I hired him a month back after a close kidnapping; to be my eye.

Security.

I start the car, blast the radio, and bob my head to the wind, the chords, and the moment. I can feel the Vodka walking through my veins. In the parking lot, I feel the weight of fate fall into my stomach like a stone. This happens every single time before a job. My heart begins to race and a sick feeling creeps along every nerve in my body. "Can't do this shit much longer," I say, reaching into the car's console for a bottle of valium, crushing a few with my teeth, feeling their bitter taste.

'You can do this. You can do this. Just a few more jobs, and you'll be done,' I amp the dolled-up girl in the mirror. And it was true. Just a few more jobs and I was out of here. Packing up and leaving it all behind with a stack of savings. *A new start*: Jasmine's ice was melting.

I step out of the car, hearing the heel of my red shoe hit the pavement first. There is a hearing power in these heels. Borrowed, yes, but isn't it all borrowed? There is something about a woman—or a man—who can walk straight in a six-inch heel. I can walk in them. Hell, I can fuck in them.

I spot Buddy, giving him the peace sign. And then stride towards the hotel's large glass doors, framed in gold. Inside, there is an indulgence to all of it, too grand really. And I wonder how this night will end—with my body bruised, hair pulled out of place, bottom lip bitten? I keep walking, despite the unknown, with my head held high, pushing my chest in and out, taking deep breaths, focusing on the tempo of my heels now clicking against marble floors. *'Spiked HEEL to the temple...'*

He—the faceless John, sits posing like a dumb prince on a bar stool. When he sees me approaching, he stands up with a face flushed. He's nervous. I keep a steady pace towards him, the beat of my heels like a drum now, imagining myself as a warrior, moving to the rhythm of their *click-clack, click-clack.*

Meeting, he offers me an unsteady handshake. I take his hand with a firm grip. My face gleams with confidence, as sweat congeals on his pale face. Maybe I should offer him a Valium. "Payment first," I say, smiling.

"Oh, of course," he says, fumbling for his wallet. He hands me fifteen one-hundred-dollar bills, fresh from some ATM—probably his father's—still stuck together.

He'll be *easy money*, and I smile knowing so, a smile he probably mistakes for genuine affection.

8

LIFE AFTER ARTICLE 370

by Sameem Hassain

August 5th | 2019

A bbu…Where are you going?"

"I am going to meet my friends," he said with a smile.

"What Abbu! You're looking a lot happier today?" I asked curiously.

"Yes beta, it's good news. Finally, good days are coming for Kashmir. The Supreme Court has declared the repeal of Article 370. Removal of those restrictions would allow businesses to expand and attract private sector investment. This will encourage our youth in Kashmir to get good jobs. Food processing and horticulture will be established," Abbu said with enthusiastic delight. That gleam in his eyes always made me smile.

This was Abbu's vision that he's been yearning for his motherland for decades. He never wanted to travel out of Kashmir. He always felt proud to call himself a Kashmiri. I still recall my childhood days when my father used to tell his friends during our morning walks, "Bhai, I was born as a Kashmiri, I will live as a Kashmiri, and will die a Kashmiri."

***

One Year Later

"Abbu, get something to eat, I'm so hungry." my sister complained.

Abbu looked troubled. Tears ran down his cheeks, mirroring his helplessness and pain, but he managed to avert his eyes.

"I'll try to get something," he assured my sister as he stepped out.

Abbu's expression was dark. His assumptions had been wrong. All his hopes and dreams were shattered. Everything around us had collapsed in Kashmir; the state was in complete lockdown and there were only a few people who benefited from the abrogation of Article 370; and those beneficiaries were the news channels, who were putting out good content and gaining high TRP ratings. We, the Kashmiris, were kept in lockdown for over a year, but the rest of the people in India couldn't handle the lockdown put up in light of COVID-19.

The abrogation of Article 370 in Kashmir brought waves of happiness and joy to people and they celebrated it like a festival, but it didn't take long for everything to change.

It had been an hour since Abbu left to find something to eat; the pandemic engulfed the country in a tsunami of pain and suffering. Here we are, fighting to fill our stomachs as only a handful of ration shops were open, due to the strict lockdown guidelines. A wave of panic washed over me; I couldn't just sit idle anymore. I rushed out to find my father.

After searching every nook and corner of the streets, I found him, leaning against a rock near a small house. It seemed as if he was in pain, holding his chest, unable to breathe. I knew the reason behind this.

I gently patted his back and said, "Don't worry Abbu, let's sell this watch; it's of no use to me." He looked up at me; I saw the pain in his eyes. He cried and hugged me.

We ran a small shop on the main street. Since our city was under complete lockdown, our business crashed. The little savings we had, went into taking care of our home. Days were getting tougher.

I sold my watch and with the little money, it got me, salvaged some food to take home.

***

"What are you doing Zafar?"

"Just browsing some online study material, dude," he said.

Somehow, I made it to my childhood friend's house while evading the cops.

"Do you still have hope for our internet, Zafar?" I asked.

People throughout the country are hyped about the 4G network, but we in Kashmir still rely on our 2G network. Due to the lack of the Internet and low data speed, the Kashmir youth lose opportunities. We don't even get work updates and related reports.

"Leave it yaar! It will take at least half an hour to load;" I said.

He laughed at my impatience. There is a saying 'Even in the hardest times; be strong enough to laugh'.

Here we were not strong, but we laughed.

Zafar opened the fridge and threw me an apple and said, "Don't drop it, these are much more precious than diamonds nowadays."

"I know I know yaar... the Apple industry, worth Rs 8000/- crores in Kashmir was badly affected and this caused Kashmir's GDP to drop after the repeal of Article 370," I said.

"What happened to the job you applied to last month?" he asked.

"The lockdown took away everything," I replied coldly, not really in the mood to talk anymore.

"Okay man, I should get going... It's getting late. Moreover, Abbu is not feeling well."

"Oh my god! What happened to him?" asked Zafar, visibly worried.

"He seems a little weak. I'll see you later. Bye."

It was dark, the moon began to glow brighter than ever providing a decent source of light; The streets were empty, no surprise there, given the curfew. My home was two blocks away from Zafar's and the time was almost 10:30 P.M. Patrolling starts at 9 o'clock. If the cops find me, they will make my life a living hell. I hurried home, making as little noise as possible with my footsteps.

***

It was around 11:30 P.M, and I was watching a movie. Ammi rushed towards me saying Abbu is feeling uneasy.

I went in and found Abbu breathing heavily. Ammi and my sister were scared, on the verge of tears.

"Don't worry mom; I'll call Zafar and we'll take him to the hospital."

I made a call to Zafar while trying to comfort Abbu.

"Don't worry Abbu; be strong, you'll be alright," I said with a quiver in my voice.

Zafar requested the ambulance, but it wasn't available at the moment. We decided to take him on the bike. Zafar was riding and I held Abbu, talking to him and making sure he didn't lose consciousness.

I was praying that God would show mercy on us. We reached the hospital yelling loudly for help.

"What happened to him?" asked one of the nurses.

"I don't know... he just collapsed while eating food, please help him... help him...." I begged, tears now streaming down my face.

"Wait, I am not the doctor here. First, you must get the COVID-19 report, if it's negative then we will move ahead," she explained.

"You need to hurry up; there is a COVID-19 test center 5 kilometers from here", she said, checking her mobile.

I was broken, Zafar patted my back, understanding my pain. Abbu was not able to travel anywhere by bike, not anymore. We didn't know what to do.

"I'll try to get a taxi," Zafar said and rushed out of the hospital.

I sat beside Abbu looking at his pale face. I felt angry with myself and my helplessness. His breathing was heavy. I held his hand to check his pulse, it was very weak.

I tried getting his attention, "Abbu... Abbu... please look at me. Abbu... can you hear me, it's your son."

There was no response from him. I yelled for the nurse loudly," Help! Nurse! Please help!" Some of the hospital staff surrounded me. The on-duty doctor checked Abbu's pulse and spoke the very words I did not want to hear, "I'm sorry son, he is no more."

"Vehicle is ready, let's make a m-" Zafar came running, almost shouting. He stopped in his tracks, shocked to see what had happened. He put his hand on my shoulder, tears streamed down my cheeks and onto his hand. I wiped my eyes and I looked at Abbu's face. The happiness and joy I usually saw in his eyes were now replaced by an unresponsive stare.

I saw no difference between the life of a hopeful Kashmiri commoner and an orchard destroyed by unseasonal snowfall.

***

One Week Later

"All set brother, the video is running, we are ready to go live in three... two... and one." Zafar pointed to me.

"Hello, my name is Farooq Ali. Yes, I'm Kashmiri; Not a movie wala Kashmiri, but an individual who has suffered. I'm not making this video to condemn anyone. I'm just here to share my feelings.

My dad is a good person. Sorry! Was a good person. Many of our relatives migrated to other parts of the nation, but my father being a patriotic man always used to say; "I'm a born Kashmiri; lived as a Kashmiri and will die a Kashmiri." Well, he was true to his word! We had the chance to live happily elsewhere but didn't. I used to consider him foolish, but now I feel proud to be his son."

My father's cries echoed in my ears, "Kashmir badlega!".

"Things may change, circumstances may change and even people may change but Kashmir won't change until our voices are raised. I hope that no one suffers like we did."

9

SHE IS THE KIND

by Ann Chaiti Sarkar

I t's the loss that gets me. The emptiness of it. How it leaves me broken and void. Like the wind could pick me up and blow it away. Like a memory. Like a ghost. Only a shell of what I was once. The product of such a troubled past. In those moments, I'm reminded that I won't always be lost. Something will come along and fill me up again. Maybe it'll be hope, maybe it'll be love. I'll never know. But either way, I know it'll end.

It's the beat of your heart that gets me. How I used to hear it like a lullaby in the dark of night. How it let mine echo in tune. Like it was a song, our song. The one I would know from anywhere. It was familiar. It was home. In those moments, I was complete, and you adhered to my dilapidated heart.

The raindrops hit the ground and melt into drains which further melt into rivers and the ocean. I want to melt into you like the river does to the ocean. I want to be more than just that triangle of rain that your windshield wipers miss on your car window, I want to be your ocean. I want to be the tide, and you the moon, forever your hypnotized and hopeless servant, ebbing and flowing with your cyclical movements like the spoon that you swirl around in your cup of coffee.

The conversations that we had in that coffee shop are ones I'll never forget. The countless times I drowned so far into your words that I became one with the bottom of your coffee mug, where even just your eye contact became something energizing, and warm, and muffling.

Laying there, at the bottom of that cup, there was nothing I could feel except for your lips pressing up against my walls to drink me in. And I knew then that you were the one who was the ocean, drinking in my rivers, one raindrop at a time.", Jane scribbled almost inattentively in her old almost tattered diary.

The mist on the window makes it hard to look outside. It was raining heavily and she just sat there at the edge of the bed with her socks on, opposite to a mirror holding her tattered old diary where she had previously scribbled down her naked raw emotions about the man, she just made love to. Her white body is wet, and steam is rising from the skin. Her wet hair has mercilessly settled down on her bosoms, ending inches above her bare back.

She is the kind who is compassionate during morning coffees but also almost ruthless by the unmistakably beautiful and still midnights.

She is the kind who whispers the language of the soul through intimacy and complains about the broken button of her shirt. She is the kind who is gentle with piano but has reckless fingers between her legs. She is the kind who hates the taste of whiskey but swigs down a bottle while partying.

She is what everyone thinks is wrong with the society, but she is everything right to The One, the One she mentioned in her tattered diary.

Every Thursday and Saturday — the days when they make love — they explore new possibilities about themselves before making love. Tonight, she is exploring herself, for her chaos.

He steps forward and they sit together on the bed, looking in the mirror.

And he whispers to her with a sincere smile, "There is something terribly sad about a cosy night where two people are not making love".

10

A DANGER TO SOCIETY

by Harshita Garrepalli

Adah Davidson's boyfriend had left her when she was nineteen. She wasn't the only person left behind, though. Their one-year-old, Mason, recognised by Adah's parents as only the epitome of his father's incompetence, was abandoned too. Adah's parents did not want to help their daughter because they were "ashamed" of her teenage pregnancy, because they came from a fairly conservative home. Adah and Mason were very poor and knew of no one who would help them in such a crisis. She did odd jobs to bring food on the table, but still wore a radiating smile on her face every day. She always told her co-workers that it was the smile on her son's face after a long day at work that motivated her to wake up every day. Since she couldn't afford a babysitter, she brought Mason along to her workplace. Her life always gave her reasons to be sad, like the night she got evicted without prior notice, but bursts of joy, when Emily, her co-worker, was kind enough to take Adah and Mason under her wing until they found a place.

Three years later, Adah and Mason were lucky enough to find a house and moved in with the little belongings they had. It was a predominantly white neighbourhood in California, where Adah and Mason, who were African American, did not feel welcome, with the frequent looks and glares thrown their way. Adah couldn't do much, after all, she needed a place to live, even if that meant social exclusion.

A few months passed in that neighbourhood, and Adah hadn't experienced anything too bad, except for the daily dose of condescending stares and Mason's exclusion from play dates and birthday parties, which, according to Adah, wasn't a big deal, because at least they still had a roof over their head. She tried to spend time with Mason, but work was always in her way and she needed the money. However, on the night of the 4th of July, Adah got off work early enough to take Mason shopping for new clothes. After billing the two shirts Adah could afford for Mason, they were leaving the store, but the metal detector beeped. Adah checked her bag for anything that wasn't billed but couldn't find anything until she looked at a very terrified Mason.

"Why are you sweating, baby?" she asked.

"Black woman, around five feet, five inches-" a voice trailed off in the background.

"Okay, miss! Put down any weapons you have and give us the shirt back." The security guard of the store said, sounding as terrified as Mason.

Mason timidly pulled out a red shirt from under his clothes.

Adah looked at the metal tag on the shirt and was taken aback.

"I-I don't have any weapons," Adah said, confused, and gave the shirt back.

She looked over at Mason.

"Baby, you stole?! Never do that again!"

"I'm sorry, mommy!" Mason cried as he sped into his mother's arms.

"It's okay, I'm sure the store owners will be kind enough to understand-"

"HANDS IN THE AIR!" a voice echoed from behind Adah.

Mason couldn't understand. Red and blue lights blinded him.

"Black woman, danger, thief." were the words echoing in his head as he saw his mother pushed against the hood of a police car with handcuffs.

"I'm sorry, officer. But please, you have to understand, it was an honest mistake, he's just a boy..."

her voice trailed off as a gun was placed to her head.

"You shut up or we take your son in." he said.

Adah slowly looked down, in compliance.

Mason finally found the courage to run to his mother.

"MOM!"

He was pushed back by one of the cops.

"Don't hurt my son!" Adah shouted.

The officer next to Adah tightened the grip of the gun as the barrel was tightly pressed against her head.

The store owner, a fifty-year-old, white man, came rushing out of the store.

"HER! From the moment I saw her, I called you, I knew she was trouble..." he said.

"Please don't shoot me. He's a child! I returned the shirt." Adah said, trying to defend herself.

One of the cashiers then spoke up.

"She gave me the look. Threatening one. She said she would kill me if I didn't let her take the shirt."

"That's not, I never-"

The officer slapped her.

"Shameless, filthy woman! THIEF! A danger to society."

"But I didn't do anythi-"

The deafening sound of a gunshot filled the air.

Mason took his hands off his ears, and he knew the dead silence after meant worse.

He stood up, towering over his mother's corpse. With filmy eyes, he cried,

"MAMA WAKE UP! WAKE UP!"

"She ain't wakin' up, son." the officer with the gun said, as his accomplices laughed.

Mason lay next to his mother's corpse the whole night, telling her how sorry he was, how much he loved her. He blamed himself for her death, and he still does.

We read such heart-breaking stories every day. Elijah McClain, Breonna Taylor, Tamir Rice, George Floyd, Ahmaud Arbery, Rayshard Brooks and so many more have given up their lives, lost their families, to make us all realize the true horrors that exist in the world and how we don't bat an eyelid. The responsibility of the people of our generation is to bring many like Mason and Adah to the justice they deserve so that no one grows up with the deepened trauma of losing their family member or the fear of getting killed because of the colour of their skin.

SAY THEIR NAMES.

Don't turn a blind eye and a deaf ear to those, whose struggles you can't feel.

We must promise a secure future to our fellow coloured people and that can only happen if we all unite with a purpose. True independence comes with the freedom of not only us but of our brothers and sisters as well.

UNITED WE STAND, DIVIDED WE FALL. WRITTEN IN PROTEST.

SYLVIA'S OVEN

by Robert Ormsby

I'm in constant awe of the poets.

How do they do it? They take the most nuanced of feelings and turn them into something tangible. They show us a thought and they voice an emotion. They see the ethereal and using their words, they give it shape and form.

And they allow us to hold it in our hands, ever so briefly.

Imagine being able to pull these things from the depths of a mind or heart and allowing it room to grow on a page. Imagine showing pieces of yourself that others would rather hide. Imagine such intimacy with all things in life and death.

I wish I were a poet. They're the only ones I know that can do these things.

The politicians of the world can't do it. They're more concerned with the holding of power, and power has no empathy or understanding.

The businessmen of the world can't do it. They're driven by money, and honesty or truth rarely pays dividends.

The hateful, the prejudiced, the angered, and the ignorant- they can't do it. They have no heart with which to speak.

The philosophers can't do it. The sound of their thoughts and ever-demanding logic drowns out the cries called out by passion and desire.

The poets see around corners.

The poets dream through their days and work while we sleep.

Poets feed from their eyes and take taste with their hands.

They walk amongst us, unbalanced and forever leaning.

There is a darkness in their light. There's a hope found in their despair.

I suppose all of our poets must be broken.

Their hearts beat slightly faster than yours or mine and their tears roll from their eyes in a backward motion. They hear voices that dare not speak to you or me.

Oh, Lady Lazarus! What is that in your oven?

Poets can change the world. They give it shape, whether in a cry for peace or a call to arms.

I fear I am too plainly to be a poet.

But I dream of you all the same.

POEMS

Equal

by Bethany Castle

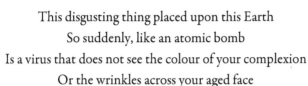

This disgusting thing placed upon this Earth
So suddenly, like an atomic bomb
Is a virus that does not see the colour of your complexion
Or the wrinkles across your aged face
Or the smoothness of your cheeks.

It does not see your slanted eyes
Or the blue eyes of a young blonde child.
It does not hear the anger in your voice
Nor does it hear the absolute fear.
It does not see the beauty in melanin
Or the perfection in porcelain pale skin.
It does not know the country of your ancestors
Or where it even came from.

This virus does not treat us as unequal.
So in this time of need we need not spit hatred
When we should be loving and protecting.
An entire race isn't the enemy
Perhaps they're suffering right beside you.

At the end of the day
This virus sees us all as equal vessels.

So why shouldn't we?

Missing

by Sybil Samuel

they found a body
breathing with lungs full of nothingness
hands tied to the oppressions of the age
his eyes blankly staring at the silence ahead
his skin bruised, full of despair
his head wounded with the injuries of expectations

they found a body
no one recognised the man
who was he
who did him this bad
what was his name
what became of the man

they found a body
hardly awake but still not dead
shoulders hanging with no more will left to fight

they found a body
choked to lifelessness
imprisoned in a doomed world who failed to hear his cry
he cried for someone to remind him of hope and care
of the light in the morning after the night engulfs him in pain and
misery

they found a body
who dreamt of a world of beauty
a world that would not wound him with sentences rude
a world of no hate, no discrimination
but a world of acceptance, love, and peace

they found a body
someone who once lived, but was forgotten for a mournful of decades
across the street with a plan of a future in bliss

there was a man, who once lived, but simply
they found a body
it was him, the man named

The Actuality

by Deepika Bhardwaj

Her amplifying daze,
Ultimately terminated,
As she perceived the unfamiliar-
Irreverent gazes, inaudible gasps.
The anomalous and subtle truth,
Was the unfolded.
Shaken out from her trance,
Aphorism seeped into her delicate frame.
Bundled with her harsh actuality,
Her vision became vague.
Profanities and curses,
Irreverence and impiety,
Surrounding her, suffocating.
Exhaling smoke, daunting flare.
A victim of unnecessary
Contempt, judgement, and glares.
She held her head high, though
Anon, her war began to defunct herself.
As her battle devastated her,
She perished in her own glory.
Only vanished for them to chant, lament-
A great soul lost, a beautiful girl gone.
She was destroyed within.
The impertinent remarks,
Murdered her efficacy.

For what, she pleaded.
For whom, she wailed.
That night, the angel soon left wandering.
In the skies, amidst her own reverie.

Alice In Wonderland

by Shama Mahajan

To walk the streets, without worrying about stalkers
To wear clothes, of a choice my own, and not the onlookers.
To scream to be heard, is no more a need
Even silence is valued, but not as consent deemed.
Where my body, is not a burden for the government to carry
Where "you are a woman", is a compliment, not derogatory.
Where change is brought, not after creating numerous victims
To be a beacon of hope, there is no precondition to endure sufferings.
Where beauty is appreciated, not commodified,
Where a face is an identity not to be destroyed.
Where virginity is a matter of choice,
Where honour cannot be sullied, by whims of the patriarchal demon.
Where justice is celebrated, not encounters
Where laws are a reality, not mere imposters.
Where compassion, isn't a rare trait
Where egos don't claim themselves to be great
Where bodies, aren't civilised to be perfect
At the cost of disfigurement by a corset,
Where voicing out concerns isn't a cause for threat.

So, may be on a day like this in the near future,
We can all celebrate
If not as the Snow Whites and the Cinderella's of this age
Waiting to be claimed by our prince perfect;
Rather as,

Women, independent to choose their own fate.
So, we can run behind the rabbit and take a leap of faith in the rabbit hole
Without worrying about being followed.
So even we can embark on our voyage of adventure and find our hatter,
For on a day like this, as I see it and understand,
This world itself will be our own *wonderland*.

The Run-Away Girl

by Deepika Bhardwaj

The little light that she'd been kindling
So carefully, so secretly,
Now guides her out, guides her away!

And how you wished that she was more obedient to you'
And to her waywardness,
This run-away girl!

You preach that her mirror should be painted black.
Or that they should have hidden away,
That jingling pair of earrings.
You accuse the scent of her nape,
'It must have her scent that charmed him
To take her away.'
What you don't see
Is the possibility
Of her eloping
With her reckless rage.

Tonight, with no man
And in no man's hope,
She flees.
This run-away girl!

She has left them behind,

Along with a bag full of snakes
your tantrums and you chains.
The earring that you so worry about
Never left its place.

You warned her
Of her soft brittle bones
Of her inadequacies.
You kept in check
Her fire, her folly her untruly itch!

Tonight, the spine of your lies crumbles,
Her madness escapes and giggles to your face.

My Body

by Rhea Choudhary

I love my body,
For I have learned to secretly enjoy my own world.
You ask, what do you mean by "own world"?
My body was ten years old,
Ready to enter the sports arena.
Just then, stretch marks came up my waist like upside down roots,
With no origin.
Only the end and no beginning.
Then my body was twelve years old.
Similar patterns came on calves and a little bit on upper arms.
Then they just grew like the rivers running on a country map,
Like protruding veins on back of a fisted hand.
Does this mean you hate the rivers on the map, your veins and roots?

I was so little to understand that they hold the opposite of whatever
beauty meant.
Sometimes, certain things are around you but you need people to
make you realize its significance.
Bodies are the perfect epitome of objection to beauty.
You don't make it, but it has its own ways;
Slim people too have stretch marks.
Now, no one can blame fat people for eating too much;
If they want, they will appear.
I tried to make it disappear, but it became more pronounced,
I blamed my body, but it was me who was adamant.

And then, my body was nineteen.
It was no longer my body, but me.
All clothes now have my blessings,
Not because they are good at hiding but,
because they are misleading.
Let my body be the dissent,
My writing be the carrier.

PSA From Your New Commanders-in-Chief

by Jacqueline Olivia

We know too well what it is
To be struck by a country
That would rather wrap us in prison sheets,
Than wrap us in its flag,
By a system who'd rather prey on our differences,
Than pray for our health.
For years upon years
Corners have been our second home;
The shadows, our solace
We've spent our whole lives playing by your rules.
No more.

You thought your boots would bury our voices,
So, you kicked us to the ground.
You thought your guns would earn you respect
So, you shot out our sight.
What you failed to recall, is that our arms linked
Are a chain that won't be burned, beaten, or broken into silence.
Undivided, we call the shots
And as your new Commanders-in-Chief,
We command,
You lower your weapons and
Put our justice where we can see it.

Inquilab

by Neha Mazumder

Saffron stained walls
Hate speech in the name of god
Gunshots in the open
Policemen stand and watch
Today the country stands divided
And we choose to still ignore
The terrors of possibilities
Are now two steps ahead of reality

I belong to a family of immigrants
My grandmother has lost all her documents
But her faith lies with the majority
So that means she is by default exempt?
I, on the other hand, sit at the tier of privilege
With the correct adjectives to define my existence
By only the virtue of my place of birth
Oh, what an efficient system of calculating worth

Don't you still recognise the poison?
The success of pitting us against us
And condemning anyone who dares to question
And take their questions to the streets
You see, xenophobia leads to wars
And we're a society of civilised humans
You see, your hatred makes you the same

As the ones you consider "them"

Look around and feel the air
The country is burning
And our people are bleeding
When is enough actually enough?
If this is what faith leads to
Then I am happy to not believe in mine.

Warrior

by Padmini Peteri

He caged her,
He bent her with his cane,
He abused her with words that pierced her soul,
He cut her wings off,
Like a bird that is only meant to be caged,
He treated her worse than an animal,
That proved what sort of a beastly beast he was,
He caned her for speaking her mind,
He caned her for being herself,
He devoured her of life,
Of basic needs,
He bent her but she did not break down,
For she was courageous,
For she believed there is light after darkness,
She was scared for her life,
But she did not give up,
To her giving up was not affordable,
He was her demon,
That sucked life out of her,
And she believed
That there will come a day,
A day when
She will mock him,
With her dauntlessness,
She will win, he will lose,

She will rise from all the thorns
That surround her,
Like a phoenix from its ashes,
She will fight like a "Warrior"
And win the battle!

Chosen

by Noelle Nams

It all started with a turmoil,
thunderstruck by a lightning bolt
and we shattered
into million pieces, billions maybe.
I didn't get a chance to choose
what I wanted,
who I wanted to be.
I trusted the powers
of the divinity.
I knew I was whole-
complete and beautiful
until others started talking
about what they got
and what they ought to be.
I was perplexed, perturbed
"What have you done?
And for what reason?"
I sought the sacred
only to see the holy radiate
brighter and abundantly on me.
Till date, I have still not understood,
"If I have been blessed
then, why have I been chosen?"
Maybe, the most favored ones
are *chosen* after-all!

Teeth of Wisdom

by Aru Deep

My wisdom tooth came in
My ma praised my worldliness, my wisdom

What wisdom had I yet to gain, ma?
That boys can be raped too?
For the household help gifted me that wisdom
At 4 years of age
Days before you gifted me with a brother

The wisdom that the world is not nice in return?
My first ever friend showed me that
When he turned away forever, to join groupies
You say kids are innocent ma
But they are cruel too

The wisdom that some are unwelcome?
The rivers of red I saw on television, fires burning
They dismissed it as communal violence
It broke my heart ma

The wisdom that money can buy everything and more?
I saw it with my eyes, ma
As they razed my friends entire colony
Tossed it aside like so much garbage

The wisdom that nature has given us?
Who even listens anymore, ma?
This wisdom you speak of has no place
In a world where the aged are not respected
In a world where the youth are not loved

We have made this world ourselves, ma
And so are we lying in it
On our own, to our own
The only wisdom I have gained is that
Even you have lied to me, ma

Responsibility

by Alexis Romo

Though you may feel
that you aren't doing enough
to help right now
and what you may be doing already
seems too small to matter,

remember that every small step
towards change and justice
is one step closer to achieving it,

for we all must carry the responsibility
to bring change,
justice,
and peace,
but we must carry it together
because we all know
it is much too big
to carry all alone

Semi-transparent Soldier

by Alison Hawes

I am made of glass,
only the glass is clouded
and has been rebuilt so many times
that it is close to bullet proof.
You can try to break me.
All you will crack is a small piece
of my outer shell.

Don't you understand?
This disguise, this cover,
is all I have.
Why would you want
to take that away from me?
Why would you want to destroy
the only thing I have left?

My new life, my new identity
was built to be strong.
I carry myself as though
I'm unbreakable, made of stone.
Sometimes, I'm not quite sure
exactly who I'm supposed to be.

Invisible

by Tiffany Lindfield

It was bitter cold last night, and we were
Starving,
Dying to eat a stick-to-your bones meal. We had found
56 cents and walked to Krystal's,
Buying one slider, settling,
Splitting it between us.

5 a.m., dog-hungry, taking a job at the
Temp Labor. Baggers at
Hobby Lobby. We are
Relieved. Last week we had been lunch ladies at some
Yuppie school, serving spoiled brats
Tacos, rice, salad, and yogurt cups
While we starved.
I got in trouble for stealing a yogurt cup from the
Trash. It was already opened. I had licked the
Strawberries from the *bottom*.

Given blue aprons, and placed with other
Cashiers at parallel registers, we
Steal encouraging glances at each other.
Wrap, and bag, wrap and bag,
Wrap, bag, *smile*. Wrap, bag, and don't
Shoot yourself.
Slaves in the spoke of capitalism's wheel.

A week before Christmas and the store is in
Chaos. Christmas, I thought—
I had forgot about Christmas,
And here it was; thrown all over this store like
Confetti and *vomit.* And the
Shift, aching hands wrapping ornament,
After ornament.
Our stomachs growling in another kind of ache. The
Gaze of our eyes casting down.

People scurrying like bees
Buying in frenzied attacks, money
Wasted on plastic stars, foam glitter balls,
Cheap angels, and tinsel,
While we ration nickels and
Dimes for off-brand bologna.

Wrapping and bagging, don't *shoot* yourself, don't
Step out of the assembly line.
Consumed products destined for landfills. The
Waste a tower of filth hidden behind
Smiles and fake Merry Christmases,
Tucking us away, like the boats of trash that float to
Poor nations. So, they can
Buy in peace. *Peace* be with you.

If we were known:
Low-life, trashy, scum, dirty, lazy, food-stampers, unworthy,
Beggar, junkie, lacks motivation, irresponsible—
Invisible.

But we eat tonight,
A stick-to-the ribs meal and
Smoke Newport Shorts.

The Mistreated Gender

by Noela Paraschiv

You say "let's go back to 1900s",
but then feminism wasn't a thing.
You forgot that my kind barely survived that time?
Don't you remember women were your slaves,
prostitutes and pets?
A beating replaced the flowers,
they just had to endure it for hours.
Wake up the next morning,
warning:
you cannot cross their word.
I've heard
this so many times.
That's what wives
have to go through...
Let's talk about the Middle East,
where our past is their present,
quite often there is a feast:
choose a woman, pick a wife,
just take more if you please.
Age doesn't matter,
an entire gender
has to go through slaughter.

Stop Domestic Violence and Alcoholism

by Arti Chopra

The evil brew called liquor
makes families fight and couples' bicker.
so skillfully it gets you in its hold,
creates miseries untold,

Soon starts the dependence,
the craving, to get that bottle,
he is ready to throttle,
to beat, to batter,
and threats that don't matter,

And you realise it's too late,
instead of cursing your fate,
it's time to take the plunge
Escape from the dirt and the grunge
make a new life, for your children and yourself,
no need to tolerate,
the beatings the abuse,

He is too weak to refuse
the drink has gripped him tight,
he has lost the will to fight
he is slave now to the evil liquid
to the devil's brew.

so run and save yourself
make a life anew
and you will emerge stronger
a shadow, no longer
of the proud and valiant woman
God meant you to be.

you will rejuvenate, revive, be reborn,
Awaken to a new morn
Leave him, let him be,
for the sake of yourself,
and your family.

Infidelity

by Ann Chaiti Sarkar

And just like that you drag me to the altar of humiliation
By doing nothing. By standing still in your adroitness and dexterity:
Being a bystander
As I text and expose new flesh of my chagrined bosom, heart's dolour
By standing, you let me and just like that you drag me to the altar of
humiliation by doing nothing.
By standing, you let me get to the stage of pleading my case;
Bystander: with a two-tick glance you swiped on by,
On standby: till I reach some boiling point of social liability:
That threatens you as 'not such a nice man'
Cliff-hanger: look into my eyes and pry my fingers off one by one.
Let me crash into the waves and break the bones of silence
That will terminate the craze of love's limerence gaze
Let this turn me into a myth that roams the shores,
And haunts the cliffs,
And beckons every forlorn lover to the edge to the end of all
unrequited abyss.
But wait. A notification.
... he is typing ...
... you are typing ...
... YOU ARE TYPING ...
STOP!
I cannot wait.
If this rescue attempt to salvage shrunken dignities is half-hearted ego
bait.

I beseech thee, therefore
Release my fingers. Thank you.
Do it. Now.

Goddesses of Nights

by Heer Dayani

I once sat under a cloudless,
Starry night, and it took me
To a place where I could feel
And sense the sculpting
Of goddesses with their elegant
Smile, crafted to save the world,
And their eyes, to bestow peace
Upon all the restless souls and
I wondered if they were always
Meant to be so graceful or it's just
The set of hands, the blessed
Sculptor possesses that does
The enchanted work.
And the next day I met a little girl,
Painted with the darkest of nights
Over her body and she told me
She had now, learnt to live in a pool
Of self-disgust, brimming
With hatred from her friends
Who were bright as a cloudless,
Sunny day, yet burnt at the thought
Of her and the moonlit sky,
Being the best mates,
So I told her a tale about goddesses
Being carved in the dark

Of the night with cloudless,
Starry sky, so to those of you
Who say, " I understand."
Say it when you mean it
Or don't say it at all.

This Name Was Given To Me

by Skyler Saunders

When I had nowhere else to turn.
When I couldn't bear the sight of
my old one—notice how I spell
things differently now that
you're gone? My entire
vocabulary has shifted to
remove any memory of you.

This name wasn't passed down
so much as chosen—paid for—
fought for—and you can't try to
tell me yours was more real.
I turned my back on ~~it~~ you.

This name was given to me,
and I went to war for it.

ARTICLES

1

WRITE WHAT YOU LOVE.
WHY DO I WRITE?

by Eileen Salisbury

I write to make sense of the world. I write to give my life meaning, in a time when it feels like a long hard slog that doesn't fit me well, like an ill-fitting dress, too tight around my shoulders and too baggy under my arms.

I write to lift myself up when I feel I have been reduced to nothing but my worn hands and weary back. I write to remind myself I am not 'just a mother' or 'just an employee'. I am also a heart and a soul, and I write to honour them when no one else can.

There was a time when writing seemed like a chore, and I did other things to avoid it because I was weighed down with the expectation that my writing had to be 'good' or had to be well-liked. Now I don't care what others think and I simply write what matters to me. I let my inner critic say what it will, but I don't let it gag me like before.

I write when the dishes are piled all over the counters and there are little puddles of clothes on the floor of every room in the house, like breadcrumbs on a trail where my children have passed through.

I write in the evening when I know I could be tidying up and if I did my morning self would be appreciative. But I write instead. Because the alternative is what almost destroyed me, what kept me in an abusive marriage, in an empty, hopeless existence that I could see no way out of, the cold dark place I vowed never to return to.

I write to feel connected to my dreams, my soul, the magic, the source of all mystery and joy. I write to feel alive, to find the light, to be the change I wish to see in my world. I write to be completely absorbed in the moment, to feel the flow, and to know that when I am no longer for this world, I gave it my all. I did what my yearning heart desired and I did not let fear, or duty, or small-mindedness steal my joy.

I write to pull myself out of the well. My writing, no matter how flawed, is the ladder I climb to the light.

2

LOOK WHAT WE'VE DONE

by Jesika Gaston

I f plants and animals could speak, I think the world would look a lot different,

I think spiders would be less scary, fears of sharks would be trivial, and trees would be more abundant.

Climate change really would be non-existent, crystal clean water would be a right and not a privilege.

I hear the earth speaking sometimes, I hear her shouting the next; she cries, and she weeps, she speaks in disaster,

Don't you hear the crashing of her footprints as she walks the fine line of "how much more can I take"?

We crack and we break her open, then wonder why she shakes in weakness, crumbling apart, rip her open, then ask why she's bleeding.

Don't you hear the roars in the distance letting out the fire, letting out the poison we've put into her?

Second-hand betrayal, to ashes, setting fire to the trees that grow from her,

The drowning sound of her tears hitting the ground, washing out towns and villages; this is not a suicide, but a homicide.

They told me that the sky is the limit, but I did not know they meant it literally,

What fools we are, running to another planet when we turned this one into a wasting ground, no one safe nor sound--

I count my days in 10s and 20s because at the rate we are going, we will need 2 earths by 2030 just to live in peace by the collateral damage that we have created.

Did you know that all it takes to murder 1 planet is 2.3 trillion tons of poisonous chemicals and 200 years?

Everything we've touched has slowly dissipated,

Oh, how patriotic and free it feels to be able to say it took us 55 years and a whole lot of absent minds to eliminate 90% of the ocean's creatures,

And only 50 to cut down 17% of the amazon rain forest, don't you see that we are the bomb, we are the tsunami, the earthquake, and the fires,

We are the 2.2 million tons of waste dumped into our waters every year, the predicted dump that will replace the ocean by 2040.

We are the natural disaster. Insult to injury, someone call the doctor! A dose of sympathy? A prescription of empathy?

Sympathy and Empathy, two things that my generation and previous generations seem to lack, doused in double shot apathy.

I do not want my children or their children's children to see the product of destruction's past;

A catalyst that I do not wish to be a part of, I'd rather be a wildfire, by that I mean all we need is one flame to ignite the shift--

You see, our society sees the problem blindly, transparent catastrophes;

We care enough to frown and shout just not enough to be the change that starts the curing.

We fill our lungs with smoke, venom laced with pride,

But maybe not pride for we don't even see that we are hurting ourselves.

How can we be the world, but also be the thing that destroys it?

I don't think spiders, sharks, and disasters should be the ones we fear,

Maybe we look in the mirror and find that the gun is pointing at ourselves,

And if we are a part of nature, how careless we are to destroy it mindlessly; if everything we could create, why obliteration?

And of everything we could destroy, why mother nature?

She's been pleading for a while to her earless children, hear her echoes screaming, crying, mother earth is dying,

By 2050, we will be able to read the words carved on her tombstone:

Humanity and destruction; peace and war,

There is no need to set your alarm anymore, for by morning, they will not sound off,

Hands too sticky to let go of habits and patterns, eyes too closed to see what we are doing.

What are we doing?

What have we done?

3

NEGLECT AGO, ACTION NOW

by Annika Hauer

An entry from a diary of mine:
15-1-2019

I really want to beat someone up right now. That sounds harsh, but I'm reading 'The Perks of Being a Wallflower', and all I want to do is give that Dave guy a brutal, striking punch. I want him to feel the pain, the hurt, the vulnerable helplessness the girl he raped felt. What, do they think we're these frail objects that can be possessed and owned? God- I'm mad right now. I feel like this writing sounds calm but I'm practically shaking, and my insides are boiling, and my left hand is curling into a fist. **We work twice as hard and get half as much.** We are dishonoured and disrespected and taken advantage of, and none of the ungrateful jerks in the world give a damn.

(Just so you know, I NEVER cuss. And yeah, I say damn is a bad word).

And then there was that scene at the end of 'All the Light We Cannot See', where those drunk Russian boys 'take turns' on those five traumatised women. They have to subject themselves to these men just to live as if their bodies are the only thing women have to offer the world. As if we are only worth what men make of us.

Well, I am done.

I want to scream and thrash and rip my hair and eyes out and instead, I'm scrawling my unruly thoughts across this poor page.

I need a break from the world. Escape to DC's Amazon.

But maybe that's just it. Maybe I need to DO something for once and get out there and... well, I don't even know. I don't have social media- I can't stand how it glazes kids' minds with shoulds and addicts them to what they could be if they only suffered a little more every day... another time, another time.

I can't just get up at our Martin Luther King assembly and speak about sexual assault and women ruling the world and how doomed and terrible we all are. Theoretically, I can, but even if I wrote something out, I think I'd either cry while speaking (which sounds weak, but I feel like it shouldn't) or never make it out of bed. So more realistically, I could help out at a support group or write a letter to someone who society decided has power, but now I'm getting tired and I think my initial burst of fiery physical anger has subsided, and as I'm writing this my hand is beginning to quiver so I think I'll go back to sleep.

But, really, what could I do?

This entry was a year and a half ago. I share it to exhibit the doubt and inaction in everyone. However, in most, you will also find an urge and a desire to make a mark, to do something that matters. Although it took me years, in the past month I have used my words and my knowledge and taken tangible steps. I led a group of students from around my school district to email a rousing video and list of demands to change our curriculum and staff training around active anti-racism. It was hard. The hours and stress and lengthy emails added up, but we got a meeting with the chief of curriculum and a response from our superintendent. Even if no change is implemented, I know for a fact we brought light to our district offices and showed students how much their voices can matter.

In no way was this experience the end, a checkmark, or even enough. If anything, it was a beginning, an opened door to opportunities that my peers and I hadn't known to exist, and a realisation of how far we have to go. However, it was also a reminder that it only takes a few to spark a fiery movement of people that reforms or abolishes the systemically corrupt society we live in. I beg everyone reading this to get their own agenda of actions started.

Change is possible.

Who are you if you're not a part of it?

4

THE SURNAME BIAS

by Kriti

C an you imagine a world without surnames? Is it difficult to imagine yourself without a surname? Are you attached to your surname because of the pride and identity it carries?

As I put forth these questions, I'd like to discuss the following view. Let me begin with my name. I am Kriti, yes, just Kriti, which means, all my identity proof – my passport, birth certificate, etc. - claim that my name is Kriti. Although I have a surname, I choose to not use it.

One of the reasons I choose to do so is because of the confusion caused by my surname. My surname has three possible spellings and due to that, I was using different spellings over time.

The second reason was that neither my parents nor my sister, none of them used the family surname. My father and mother use their middle names as their surnames and my sister also has her first name on all official documents. Using a surname would make me the black sheep and so, I dropped my surname - only to find that choosing to not have a surname made me the black sheep everywhere I went. Slowly with time, I was able to realize the importance of surnames in our society or rather the 'need' and 'necessity' of surnames in our society.

Now when I look at the idea of certain perceptions, biases, and the family identity attached to the surnames, I feel very proud of the fact that I don't use a surname, and in turn, do not promote such differences in society.

I can tell that not many of you are convinced, and for you, I have gathered the following points:

Caste and Religion: We all consider casteism to be a curse in Indian society. I'm sure that there are many instances wherein you have fallen prey to this systematic discrimination. Here, I ask you - have ever noticed that people assume someone's caste by taking a look at their surname? At least once in your life, you would have seen this in practice. If we dig deeper into this, we can assume that surnames are the root cause of discrimination based on caste and religion in our society. It is because of our surnames that casteism has been able to survive for this long. On the assumption that Wikipedia provides factual information, we can find that a page on Wikipedia under the title, 'Indian Family Names' will give you a list of surnames segregated state-wise and caste-wise. This, according to me, is where discrimination begins. If people from different castes and religions are to stand together in normal attire, their surnames are the only means by which their caste or religion will be revealed. Subconsciously, we as a society are attached to our surnames so much that we don't realize the discrimination it brings with it.

Perception and Stereotype: We all happen to form perceptions about something without actually knowing all about it. We usually claim that India is stereotyped by foreigners, but why do we fail to talk about the stereotypes done by us? When we look at certain surnames which we assume as belonging to a certain community (that community may or may not relate to caste, religion, or state) we form a perception of that person based on the stereotypes of that community and then we start judging the person based on their community and background. Forming these perceptions is done subconsciously, almost like it's encrypted in our system.

Identity: A surname is always associated with the identity of the family and the identity of the ancestors. In my opinion, I don't agree with the need to carry either the good or bad identity given to a group of people that we have never met. Your own identity can be lost by portraying a false image under the shadow of the identity of your family. There is a very common saying in India, that a child is known by his/her parent's identity in the initial stages of his life, and the parents always wish that in the future, they are known by their child's name or reputation. This to me seems very irrelevant because identity is supposed to be someone's own and is not meant to be dependent on anyone else. In our society, the identity that the surnames carry is more like a claim on the other person. For example, a woman is supposed to change her surname after marriage, showing the husband and his family's claim on her identity. Hence, we see that for a woman, it's the identity of her father or her husband that is attached to her name. This brings our focus to the prevailing male domination or the patriarchal system in our society. In my personal opinion, I am against this concept of changing one's surname after marriage, as it objectifies women. It shows her as merely a property, that is transferred from family to family. Another fact that I want to shine light on, is that many people put their mother's name or their father's name as their last or middle name. Discriminating between parents is very illogical and would promote a bias with either choice.

Requirement: Society demands a surname as if it's a necessity. When I say this, I speak from personal experience. If you don't use a surname for official documents, you will face many problems. For every small thing, surnames are required and considered compulsory. Here I would like to point out the difference between the surname and the last name. Commonly, both these words are used interchangeably, but a surname is usually a family name, whereas the last name can be anything. Due to security reasons and identity frauds, the last name column is mandatory everywhere, however, this doesn't mean that you have to use your family name as your last name just because it's the common practice prevalent in society. You can use your first name as your last name. In my experience, there were many times when I used my first name in the mandatory last name column. Hence, there is no need for a particular surname that promotes discrimination based on caste and religion.

Changing a surname on official documents is a very hectic and chaotic task in itself. That brings me to the issues a married woman faces, one who has chosen to use her husband's surname as her last name. In the beginning, the marriage certificates act as proof of the new surname, and with time, all her documents, like her passport, driving license, bank accounts, etc. have her husband's surname as hers. As a social and individual person, she faces an identity crisis due to the huge change she faces after her marriage. For starters, she is referred to as Mrs. (her husband's surname). These small. and what we consider trivial practices, are what make the larger conversation of gender equality prominent.

Further, I would like to point out the struggles, a divorced woman faces. According to various laws in India, a married woman is 'allowed' to keep using her husband's family name, but only if the husband agrees to it. For someone facing the challenges of a divorce in a society which blames the female for it, she is pulled in many different directions and faces a lot of complications legally and socially. To top it off, she then has to change her name back in all of her documents, making the divorce an even more torturous time.

At this point, you might argue that out of all the issues in the society, ranging from corruption, lack of security for women, urban-rural development, etc., why do surnames matter? I think, here, we must remember that the tiniest hole in a boat can sink it. In the same way, no issue is small enough to be ignored. I am not asking you to take big and major actions on surname-based discrimination, I am merely asking you to think about it and be aware of its existence.

I would like to conclude by saying that India is a free country, and we are all entitled to our own opinion. I write this to raise an issue important to me, in hopes that maybe, you will consider it or that it will resonate with you. In the same way, I hope you raise issues that are important to you, that may one day, change the system for the better. Remember, every thought counts.

5

GROWING PAINS

by Jennifer Meyers

Sometimes, you're 27, staring out of the car window on another seemingly endless commute to work, wondering if the cars surrounding you feel the hustle and bustle of city life as tedious as you. As you become engulfed in a wave of nostalgia and reminisce on simpler days, like family game night or grandma's infamous chocolate chip cookies. Days where you found comfort in your mother's hugs and exhilaration in pure moments. Suddenly you don't feel at home in your skin and you want to go back to mom's, but mom's doesn't feel like home anymore either. You reflect on old situations that no longer bring solace. When sentimentality becomes too much, you take a deep breath and think about the woman you have flourished into, what it took to get her here, and how she never let the hardness of the world taint her soul. You start to feel a sense of ease wash over you when you recognize the value of who you are becoming, and that the world is in desperate need of more people like you.

You realise...

You are home.

6

ABOVE ALL WE ARE HUMANS

by Nagasri M.N

I was dominated because I was Indian?
I was brutally killed because I was black?
I was suppressed because I was a girl?

Hindu, Muslim, Christian,
The white or the black.

When the Britishers ruled us, freedom fighters fought for independence. This is what we have been taught from schooling, isn't it?

So, what kind of independence, do we have right now?

While we still celebrate Independence Day and Republic Day every year,

There are people who kill people who are black.

There are people who dominate her because she's a girl.

There are people who think women are just toys.

There are people, who don't care if it's a child or a girl or a woman.

There are people who kill another because of differences in their nationalities.

Who gave you the right?

Who the hell gave you the right to take the life of another human being?

The recent movement 'Black Lives Matter' has helped fight against racism. Yet, while protests and rallies go on, we have insensitive people walking the streets.

Did you ever wonder, why?

Is there something we lack?

Yes, we do.

We are afraid.

We are afraid because we might get involved in complicated situations.

We are afraid to take the risk.

We are afraid to raise our voice because we don't consider it our problem.

What we are lacking is that we don't go against it until it affects us.

Choose today, to be a **warrior**.

Fear not my dear,

What you do today is for a better *tomorrow*.

Every life on this earth that lives happily,

Because of you, will be holding you in their hearts,

That's how you live on for an eternity, my friend.

Raise your voice when you see something that is not right.

Raise your voice,

Because 100 years lived without helping the needy,

Is nothing in front of a day lived by helping the needy!

Nature doesn't differentiate between colour, gender, nationality,

All we have is one race, called the human race.

Today I chose a pen as my weapon to raise my voice against brutality.

Are you with me?

Come, let us fight for the human race.

Let's stand together, I'm with you.

LOVE MORE

by Jennifer Meyers

I'm sorry I was fixated on all the wrong things to nourish your soul with soil that would have helped you prosper into a woman that is fierce and unstoppable. I'm sorry I neglected your self-development on a quest to seek love from an outward source when all I needed was to look inwards. I'm sorry if all those experiences derailed you. Sorry for only exposing your most superficial assets when you are a woman of intellect and depth.

I'm sorry for the toxic, dead-end situations you invested your heart and soul into.

I'm sorry if you ever believed a message that you are unworthy, you are worthy!

I'm sorry your roots weren't sturdier to get up and walk away from places where you were not valued or appreciated.

I'm sorry I fed you darkness when you needed light and hatred when you needed love.

I'm sorry it took a decade to learn that you have not been depleted of love, only grown wiser as to whom you share it with.

I'm sorry you've become a wilted flower starved of the most basic elements for growth, but you're better now and it's time to foster a new garden with deeper roots and stronger roses.

I HAVE KNOWN

by Aeryn Perez

I have known shameful facets of man from the first year of my existence.

I have to live with the vestiges of a rare disease: **Marfan Syndrome**.

"Too tall", "too thin", I quickly learned that children's candour is a myth. There remains in each of us this instinctive, unconscious, animal functioning - we remove the disturbing element, the one that upsets the balance. I experienced it through the insignificant moments of my daily life. It starts slowly, with a girl who refuses to play skipping rope with me because of my height. It ends in incredible psychological violence.

Imagination has become my faithful companion of resistance. I had to justify my existence. Through my musical sensitivity, through my brilliant studies.

Nobody should have to do this.

As a teenager, bending under contradictory injunctions ("Be proud of yourself!"; "you are disgusting"), I bowed like a person of great age. It is now a daily struggle to get back on my feet. I denied this body that I didn't know and that was causing me so much trouble. Exclusion – insidious but growing – invites itself even into the street, where indiscreet eyes are experienced as a perpetual intrusion. Those who claim to never judge by appearance are the same who reject my body, and therefore my person. The adults, forgetting the rules of politeness that they were proud to teach me, stare at me without saying "hello".

"Ignore them"; "they are jealous" – so many empty words that have been repeated to me, denying what I was feeling.

At twenty-one years old, insults still hurt me. I can't ignore them, and I don't want to pretend they don't exist. I hate just as much false compassion, condescending pity.

But I don't claim to be different, or to be normal – none of these words can define my identity.

I only demand respect for the human person that I am, and for what I have endured so far.

9

THE DANGERS OF MISEDUCATION

by Annika Hauer

A h, ah, why is she screaming?"
Hostile, bitter laughs. The seventh-grade boy looks down at something.

"I don't know, she must like it,"

Oh, these boys; beyond me what they're on about.

Wait-

Oh my. Jesus, I will rip out their throats.

So, I did; with twenty-six letters I crafted my shield of strength and sword of anger. I whipped words to the page, filled blue lines with the horror in my heart. I asked them why, why the jokes about things that are not funny, like race and pain and-

I asked them how, how can you live with your crass selves? I wrote of my own fear, all of our fear, as women, and how we continue to fight on. Thousands of years, you oppress us, shove us into the house, into-bed. Tell us to be quiet.

And they think it is funny. I know boys can be dense and I know these ones are going through puberty, but can they not have some sensitivity? At least in school? Math class?

I planned to slip the paper, unsigned, into one of their backpacks or binders. By fate, they would find it and read it and maybe even change, but I was too scared.

For what, I could not comprehend or admit, but I was afraid and cowardly, and worst of all, quiet.

Again.

I think every human who has ever gone to public school as a kid experienced this, but these boys would also take my pencil pouch. Nothing important in there, except on the month mark.

So, one day they are stealing a pencil, and I think they see my tampon because they return the pouch to me and never take it again. It was my worst nightmare, at first; complete mortification. And then it was nice for them to leave that piece of my school day alone. And then I had this overwhelming thought:

We live in a world where it takes the discomfort of miseducation in a man to make him stop disrespecting a woman.

And even then, most continue without learning our science.

This angry fuel kept me alert to listen for harassment in their words.

So, one day, I am sitting at my table group and one of them is there and he calls me a feminist in a negative context, and it is small, but I feel strong as I say, "Why is being a feminist bad? Feminism is believing in equality."

Of course, he was referring to how social media decides to interpret it, which is that women think we are superior and wish to have power over men.

Which is manically absurd, why would we oppress when we know what that feels like? And our being the bigger person is not supposed to denote superiority but make the world a little kinder. Is that so radical that to some it feels like evil?

I told him off and he said, "That's fair," and I know nothing about him, but he treats me like I'm an equal and am just as capable and smart, so I go with the notion that he is a good person in need of some guidance, beneath all the hair gel and insensitive jokes.

The paper was never laid eyes on again. I lost it. I really wish I had it, I remember making some good points, but I lost it. Last day of school, one moment it was in my backpack and I was making a trash run and then I never saw it again. I hope a janitor, or someone found it, but the reality is that it probably found the dump.

This year I was a freshman, and though high school is nothing like the movies, there is an undercurrent that is. Drugs, sex, popularity - but of course, it does not show in everyday life. You have to look for it, or you're unfortunate enough for it to find you.

I was on a youth group retreat with the church my family attends. We've been sleeping and eating together for forty hours straight, all very feely and tired but also blissfully full of love (Believe what you want, but I'm not religious so that was not a reference to God).

I am sitting on a bed with another girl my age, across from a bed supporting a girl lying down and another one sitting with her legs hanging off the frame. She starts talking, and somehow it gets to the night and waking up and the aftermath.

My friend was raped. The people there called it unconscious sex- they said she never yelled rape, so it wasn't. She had to get an abortion and she said it hurt like hell, and by the time her words stop I am sitting next to her in a side hug and gasping for teary air.

Twenty minutes later, we are at the meeting place and everyone is sitting and looking at one of the chaperones, six years older than I am, and she starts talking and I have heard her story before but not the part where- "six months later, I was raped. I thought it was my fault. I was supposed to be clearer; I shouldn't have been drunk; I shouldn't have been there at all-, so I did not tell anyone for months. And then I did, and now I'm here, laying the most vulnerable parts out for you all to judge, but I know you won't, because I know you all, and you are people I can trust."

I have never been raped, but two people and most likely many, many more I know have been. Sexism is ingrained in society. I know this will change, eventually. Someday. Though for now the man at the gas station still flicks his eyes to the rise in my shirt. Women are still paid sixty-three cents to the dollar of a man, children are trafficked, and abortions are illegal.

To the oppression that mocks us every day, I say: you will not win.

We are too strong, too united, too angry, and outspoken, and *fed up*. We say, **enough**. No more. To the oppressors; the rapists, the sexists, the cheaters and traffickers, and jokers, *and the boys who will be boys*: **you can only run on hate for so long.** We will abolish you, **together.**

10

THE LGTBQIA+ COMMUNITY AND ITS ACCEPTANCE

by Harshita Garrepalli

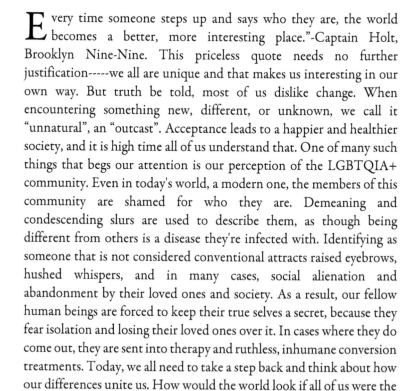

E very time someone steps up and says who they are, the world becomes a better, more interesting place."-Captain Holt, Brooklyn Nine-Nine. This priceless quote needs no further justification-----we all are unique and that makes us interesting in our own way. But truth be told, most of us dislike change. When encountering something new, different, or unknown, we call it "unnatural", an "outcast". Acceptance leads to a happier and healthier society, and it is high time all of us understand that. One of many such things that begs our attention is our perception of the LGBTQIA+ community. Even in today's world, a modern one, the members of this community are shamed for who they are. Demeaning and condescending slurs are used to describe them, as though being different from others is a disease they're infected with. Identifying as someone that is not considered conventional attracts raised eyebrows, hushed whispers, and in many cases, social alienation and abandonment by their loved ones and society. As a result, our fellow human beings are forced to keep their true selves a secret, because they fear isolation and losing their loved ones over it. In cases where they do come out, they are sent into therapy and ruthless, inhumane conversion treatments. Today, we all need to take a step back and think about how our differences unite us. How would the world look if all of us were the same? Boring, bland, and lifeless. 'Incredible India'-----why is it called that? India has a rich history and cultural heritage, different languages, religions, rituals, and customs----that vary from state to state, region to region. If the variations in a country are celebrated, what stops us from celebrating the varying preferences and identities of individuals?

There have been many brave people who have raised their voices in the matter of discrimination against the LGBTQIA+ community. The earliest of them was Karl Heinrich Ulrichs, who was a civil servant forced to resign in 1854 on the account of his homosexuality. He became an activist and published twelve volumes of work about sexuality. He put forth his argument of it being an 'inborn condition' and not a learned corruption or a disorder-----as was believed at the time. In 1867, he urged the German government to repeal anti-homosexuality laws, which crowned him the pioneer of the gay rights movement. Harvey Milk was the first openly gay person elected to public office. Magnus Hirschfeld is considered the father of transgenderism, once being described by Hitler as 'the most dangerous Jew in Germany'. Whereas Barbara Gittings is considered the mother of the LGBT civil rights movement. India doesn't fall back in LGBT representation and activism either. Ancient Indian texts are relevant to modern LGBT causes. Rigveda, one of the four ancient texts of Hinduism contains the phrase, 'Vikriti Evam Prakriti', which translates to 'What seems unnatural is also natural'. Some scholars believe this recognises homosexual/transsexual dimensions of life. The ancient Indian text 'Kamasutra' dedicates a complete chapter on erotic homosexual behaviour. More recently, after putting up a valiant and stern fight, on September 6, 2018, the Court ruled unanimously in Navtej Singh Johar v. Union of India that Section 377 was unconstitutional "in so far as it criminalises consensual sexual conduct between adults of the same sex."

This news sparked joy in the faces and lives of the members of the LGBT community again.

Even after the decriminalization of same-sex relations, people in India continue to shame the members of the LBTQIA+ community for being "abnormal" and a "contagious threat". People from the transgender community are dehumanized, called immoral, and whatnot, just because they wanted to identify as someone that they weren't born as. The world has a long way to go, to learn and unlearn a lot of things, to accept change. To start believing that not being heterosexual is normal, two women holding hands and kissing is normal, being nonbinary is normal, that trans men are real men and trans women are real women. That sex is assigned at birth, and gender is a social construct, based upon self-perception and expression, mostly why the trans community is not able to express themselves fearlessly— because of the lack of awareness of this fact to the people. As human beings, it is our duty to be willing to learn from each other and spread awareness in order to, one day, change how the world thinks, to understand that changing our opinion after learning something new is normal, that diversity is prudent and reanimating because our greatest challenge is *change*. No human being is inferior because of who they choose to love, or who they choose to identify as. All human beings deserve equal respect, and I believe that one day, we all will come to terms with it.

#LoveIsLove

POEMS

Colour Isn't A Crime

by Mythili M. U

BLACKLIVESMATTER

As a cop car approaches coloured in assumption
His heart sinks knowing that this might be the final goodbye
He grips the steering wheel, throat burning,

As two officers (bullies) walk towards him in a uniform,
The fabric sewn by threads of racism;
Their hand reflexively reaches the holster
Like dark skin was nothing less than a sin, a crime

He does not resist, simply tries to reason,
But to the bullies in the blue suit,
every word he says is nothing less than a confession.
His hands are weapons even when in the air,
His body, a target that bullets are attracted to.

He has been taught by the past,
And the names that are now lost,
To never look confident on streets.
To never wear his melanin coat with pride.
Made to believe that porcelain skin is superior.
To always look at the ground (where he shall soon be buried)
That he shall be treated more like a problem than human.

He only dreams of living long enough for his grand kids
To see him alive, to teach them otherwise
To tell them to be proud of the dark flesh that covers their white
bones
To assure them that they are worthy of life and all the wonderful
experiences
That white kids get to exploit
To prove to them that young black boys can live to be old men
And that THE ONLY DIFFERENCE BETWEEN BLACK AND
WHITE
ARE THE SHADES THAT LIE IN BETWEEN THEM.

Black Man

by Padmini Peteri

To the black man,
You are not meant to be a thug,
A gangster, barbaric, a brutal or a violent person,
You are meant to be all things good,
For you have the purest of heart, purest of soul,
Strongest of dedication
Towards your woman, your children,
Towards the people of your race, towards humanity,
Few evil people labelled you "Violent",
Because they know what
Heavenly characteristics your made of,
They are afraid that you will gain glory,
Afraid you will gain acceptance, recognition, fame,
Hence, they labelled you as a black savage,
But you know what you are,
What auspicious things you are made of.
Remember, your ancestors struggled every day
To fight for the freedom you own,
Now that you have what your ancestors dreamt off,
Do not let those few white men
Who are against your race judge you,
Do not let them tame you,
Be the extraordinary person
Because your ancestors fought for you,
With their sweat and blood,

The freedom, the opportunities,
You have now may or may not be huge,
But it is a lot more than what your race
had not long ago.
Cherish the freedom,
the opportunities,
The peace, the love,
Cherish yourself
For black man,
You are not a savage,
You are a *Gentleman*!

Hate Is Stronger Than Love

by Neha Mazumder

Sometimes influences create a stain
The stain grows darker and spreads
And then suddenly it's bigger than us
It consumes us whole
We learn to hate, and kill
We love to hate, and kill
You see, all throughout history
Civilisations have reformed
And empires have grown stronger
Religion has evolved, intertwined
But only humanity has lost its humankind
To discrimination
To suffering
To hate
You say our diversity is our pride
Then why do you succumb to the fascist regime?
It's you who loses when you kill
It's us who lose when we kill
You see, all throughout history
Civilisations have been destroyed
And empires have been demolished
Religion has been exposed, politicised
But only humanity has loved its humankind
That is why you and I are here today
Irrespective of our colours and roots

The sooner you realise the better are your chances to stay alive
For what you use to kill
Will kill you as well
For in fact if you learn to love
You can survive as well

Because of His Skin

by Jacqueline Olivia

Because of his skin, he is a liar
Because of his skin, he is a thief
Because of his skin, he is a murderer
Because of his skin, he deals drugs
Because of his skin, he is on drugs
Because of his skin, he owns a gun
Because of his skin, he is dangerous
Because of his skin, he is a monster.

No.

Because of his skin, he is honest
Because of his skin, he is kind
Because of his skin, he is wise
Because of his skin, he is strong
Because of his skin, he is loving
Because of his skin, he is passionate
Because of his skin, he is beautiful
Because of his skin, he is human too

Still Fighting

by Alison Hawes

We hold our heads high
as this villainous world hurls
its worst punches our way.
we only have armour to protect us,
and it's wearing thin.
I'm not sure how much time I have left,
but I'll stay no matter what.

I promised him I wouldn't leave,
no matter how often
every bone in my body
begs me not to.
Giving in his not an option.
I will clench my fists and scream,
but there is no way
I'm giving up that easily.

Use Your Voice

by Alexis Romo

You may be timid and afraid to speak aloud,
but now is not the time to be afraid,
for the world is divided
and we must stand in solidarity,
we must stand united.

You may not have a commanding voice
or the ability to lead the revolution,
but if you're like me, you can write.
You still have a voice -
you can still participate in this fight.

So, for those who are timid and afraid to speak aloud,
remember that you still have a voice -
you can still be a part of the revolution and the plan.
Just please use your voice,
as loud as you possibly can.

-Alexis Romo

Belly Up

by Tiffany Lindfield

"Look," Sara, my sister, screeched,
Pointing down, dramatically, eyes wide.
Fisheyes peered back.
If you stare into the abyss long enough—it will stare back.
Jerking back, "What the hell?"

We surveyed the horrid scene.
Running along the drainage ditch,
Laid their bodies, bellied up; one eye up.
The other eye down.
Sara bent down to pick one up.
"No!" I screamed— "There're dead. Germs!"
"I'm going to be a doctor one day."
"Fair enough, but don't touch me."
Sara touched one fish.
Then me.

We continued to walk.
"At least three times around," we had said.
"Chemicals and all this damn pollution,
Everything is *dying*—the whole planet," I despair.
"Let's go back! I want to know what caused this," Sara demanded.
"We did. All our greed. All this death and for what? Plastic!"

Sara, unconvinced, turns around; I followed.
We surveyed the scene again.
"The flood—they got caught in yesterday's flood!
Not the biblical flood that never happened,
But yesterday's flood done them in," I said.
Sara rolled her eyes. "The flood that never happened?"
Both eyes.
"Climate change. Like I said, we did it."

It floods all the time now, here, where we live.
Water is everywhere.
Greta Thunberg says: *Our house is on fire.*
Robert Jensen says: *Our planet is dying.*

"You said chemicals at first."
Flutter of a fin.
"One is still alive!" Sara exclaimed,
Grabbing the dying fish, rushing it towards the water,
Us watching it drop in, and *swoosh*—swim away!

"There must be more!"
Our eyes primed to see life, we saw fish tails fluttering and
Small mouths gasping for air everywhere.
Fish after fish, rushing them back to their pond.
Back and forth, back, and forth.
"Dozens to save!"
Some past the point of saving.
Hardened to a fate—one that once promised
A bigger pond. *More.*

Sun sitting behind us, and we panted.
"Only you would drag me into saving fish." Sara said,
"Global warming," I said,
Sara rolled both eyes again. "Weather."
"Nasa must have it all wrong," I shot back.
And so, it went,
Me wondering: How many more hands needed,
For the next *flood* or
Fire.

He For Human

by Yashika Tomar

Sometimes the knight loses his grip,
And falls off the horse.
When goodness of a villain gets eclipsed,
As he crosses over to the dark thoughts.
Sometimes the tender son of a butcher gets whipped,
For instead of the long meat knife, it was a little paint brush that he
bought.
Sometimes the fearless wishes to be saved,
For having lost all battles that he fought.
There's a reason we don't call him beguiling,
Sometimes it's a man who falls for mean, conniving plots.
If only we could discard the rotten point of view,
Just because we're made to believe doesn't make it true.

A Story Way Too Common

by Noela Paraschiv

Drowning my sorrow in tequila glasses
till I can't control my body,
I'm at a party I don't want to be at.
He pulls me into the boys bathroom,
covering me with kisses,
brutally.
This is not a love story; I'll tell you that.
This is the story of when I lost my faith in love,
shoving his hands under my dress.
I don't want this.
I can't stress it enough,
but that's what girls get when caught
by someone who doesn't perceive
that no is no
and at that moment
we just pray that he will leave.

Lilith

by Alison Hawes

Her fierce gaze haunts my every move.
When will she tear me apart again?
My room fills with blackness, red glowing eyes.
The air chills as goosebumps rise on my frail arms.

The woman smiles mercilessly.
Her hands spring sharp, golden claws.
The frigid water stings against tear-stained skin.
She will not leave until she gets what she wants.

Subtle

by Yashika Tomar

She is many things but subtle,
An argument with no room for rebuttals,
Like dry twisted leaves in a late windy night rustle,
In a world full of drifting hope, she's ever brimming with hustle.
Where people find reasons to pit against one another,
She lives with peace and conflict thriving together.
She observes all crooked roses bent by winter's trace,
Yet her eternal summer never fades.

Never Gatsby's Girl

by Alison Hawes

I always wish I could fly,
and in dreams, I do.
With my own two wings, I soar
up, up, and away from this nightmare.
I say goodbye
to this pathetic, plastic town
filled with manicured, plastic people
who surely lost themselves long ago.
It hurt to admit it,
but I lost myself, too.
The thing about me, though,
is I want her back.
Do they even know who they lost?
Has it hit them yet?

They throw their knives
with great force and even better aim,
but I will die before they take my wings.
They only want to change me.
I will never be like gorgeous Daisy,
so plastic and theatrical.
How could one expect a girl
to subject herself to such torture?
That will not be me.
I assure you.
I will be free.

Pick Your Poison

by Sharron Green

Pick your poison, choose your views,
where d'you like to get your news?
Want to hear the same old spiel?
Scared to face up to what's real?
Don't absorb what tabloids proffer,
just to get the special offer.
The echo chamber, at first fine,
becomes dreary over time.
Everything is sickly sweet
when the angle's not discreet.
If trash is all that you consume,
you're destined for a certain doom.
Don't be complacent or judgmental,
a balanced diet's fundamental.
Spice it up with news that's broad,
the pen is mightier than the sword.
This world seems crazy, right off course,
coz news is filtered at the source,
Don't let your brain cells go to waste -
cultivate a varied taste.
Then news won't land with such a thump,
like Brexit or the vote for Trump.
So go for pure and unrefined
and try to keep an open mind.

A Difficult Lesson

by Alison Hawes

Sometimes, I wish we couldn't feel pain,
but then, I suppose we have to.
Wouldn't we all, slowly but surely,
become addicted to what we had lost
and try anything and everything in our power to get it back?

And maybe we wouldn't learn
from our mistakes like we're supposed to.
We'd become cursed to re-enact
the same patters time and time again,
no matter how bruised and broken our hearts became.

So maybe I need this,
the knives and fists breaking down walls and working their way
into my already blackened heart.
Maybe this is it.
This is how we get through life.

I remember when the words
"When I grow up" changed to "If I grow up".
This world is built to destroy you.
You adapt or turn to dust.
Choose your battles.
That's how you make it.

Every day is a new chapter
in a game you might not win,
but that's no reason
to lay down your sword.
Shouldn't it be one more reason
that you can keep fighting?
Even if it's just for one more day?

I Am A Misfit Pariah

by Usama Bin Tanveer

I am a Muslim, I am a Jew
Vow I for those, the oppressed, the few
I am a Buddhist, I am a Christian
Vow I for those, the recipients of affliction
I am a Sikh, I am a Hindu
Where I belong, I have no clue
I am a Sunni, I am a Shia
I might be called a misfit Pariah
I am white, I am black
You might subject me to ceaseless flak
The affliction is real, no fiction
Clear it is from the gory depiction
The depiction worldwide
of a ruthless tide
against those in numbers humble
Before the whims of tyranny, they don't stumble
Instead, they choose to fight
sans any fright
Because they believe in
the God's Light
For, God is of both the majority, the minority
"*HE* never ordained racial superiority".

That Black Woman From The South

by Padmini Peteri

She saw her family being sold like cattle,
She was treated like a sexual savage,
She was labeled as a black slave,
Bought and sold like commodity,
Who was exploited every single minute,
Raped, forced to breed
And caned until she no longer wanted to live,
But she lived every day in piercing pain,
She was an object in white man's eyes,
An object to fiddle with as long as
They could gratify their sexual needs,
Her son was sold off to work in the fields,
Her daughter to a pervert white man,
Her husband was lynched to death,
She suffered in the south every second
She drew breath,
Dying everyday of her existence,
Dreaming of a freedom, of a life
Which was only imaginable in her dreams
She worked in the fields nonstop,
And the moment she wanted to rest,
She was flipped, whipped, unzipped, and stripped
Which made her want to die of the excruciating pain,
But she continued living,
In pain, in sorrow, in despair.

Hoping one day she will be free
And dreamt of liberation that was far fetched
And died of an unfulfilled freedom.

We The Mad

by Aparna Goswami

Sitting here under the unabashed naked starry sky,
Listening to the crickets and rattle of glowing bugs.
And I realise how the ways of this world are absurd
The monotonous lifestyle
The rhythmic blinking of blinded eyes
The office cubicles and bleached multistorey coffins
The most valued minted paper for which the wasted greens
The forgotten beauty of swirling sunrays kissing your cheek
The incessant typing and the speed
The wired mechanical movements from living beings
The people who made such grotesque things are the real mad

Not the ones who dare to dream,
the ones venturing into their passions deep.
Not the ones loving without restrain
Or the ones unafraid of being different.
Not the ones travelling the roads undiscovered
Or those who revolt against being hushed or covered.
Not those labelled mad and abnormal for daring to be raw.

And if doing what I want and saying what I say is considered to be
mad, then be it so.
I am not going to obey in fear
Or let you tell me what to wear.
Calling me mad will just give me more freedom

Because the mad have no blinding rules, no stringent ways of life
We are not expected to behave a way, to earn or strive
Here, we stand fighting to be free
To be honest and truly me
Because those who have the courage to roam astray
Know both, how to fight and pray.

Change

by Alexis Romo

The oppression is progressing with no end in sight,
the oppression is always building and there's always a fight–
There's always tension, there's always a war
against everyone:
against the indigenous,
against the ghetto,
against the poor.

And the wars keep going and the soldiers are being deployed,
and the bodies rack up and lives are constantly being destroyed.
And it's a constant cycle of oppression and inequality
and racism and misogyny –
it's never-ending as long as there's two opposing sides
unless we can somehow all come together and unite

but there's always a disagreement and debate about what's right and
what's wrong –
why can't we just peacefully agree to disagree and move on?
But it's come to the point where we cannot simply agree on anything
and there's no longer any social harmony

so instead we are forced to protest and to debate and to fight for what
we believe is right –
we are forced to stand up for ourselves and speak our minds.
But sometimes some of us are afraid to speak up

for we may be attacked with violence or be condemned by the law
and if that's the case,
then why do we have the First Amendment at all?
And yet we still stand up and do what we can to effect positive change
so we can hopefully end the world's suffering and pain,
which is what needs to be done if we want to make a difference
and rid the world of violent bitterness.

So, if you want your voice to be heard and for the hate to cease,
speak now
or forever hold your peace.

Voice of Nature

by Jagruthi Kommuri

You cut down all the trees,
You let the forests fire,
You leave us all homeless,
You make us all feel tired;

You pollute all the oceans,
You let all the rivers dry,
You make advancements to purify, but
One day, the water you have is only of your cry;

You let the glaciers melt down,
You let the climate change,
You are the reason for global warming,
And think the world's getting strange;

It's not just that we are endangered,
Also, humans this is true,
You think that someone would change this,
Forgetting you are that someone too.

Rebirth

by Alison Hawes

I'm not sure when I began to feel trapped
in this prison of a one-horse town
Its citizens disguised it as a safe haven.
A sanctuary.
I know that when those days began,
there was close to know way
to stop the drowning,
the pain,
and nightmares
that snuck in with it.

Chains pinch and bruise my skin
as they wrap tighter and tighter.
Will I ever break free from my captors?
Demons laugh from their dark corners,
praying that this is the day.
They will finally take me down
and add my bruised, blackened heart
to their infinite collection.

Well, maybe I learned something
from their torment.
I don't break so easily anymore.
Watch me rise from the ashes,
a phoenix blazing,
coated in white hot flames.

Discrimination Continues

by Padmini Peteri

400 years and the wars persist,
Wars of hatred, of oppression,
Of discrimination,
Are we not human?
Our ancestors went through the Atlantic Slave Trade
Indentured labour and what not,
Isn't all the suffering enough?
Why doesn't it make sense?
That we are people whose
Skin might be dark but hearts fairest,
We have sass in our language,
That others try to ape,
Our contribution to music is boundless,
Would you prefer to live a life with no music?
We own a rhythm that heals people,
The rich culture, the rich heritage
Is what makes us special,
You might try to shut us down,
Stomp us, degrade us,
But we will fight this,
We will fight for justice
and we may turn into ashes today
but remember,
Tomorrow,
We will rise like a phoenix!

Menstruation

by Mythili M. U

My inner thighs, faintly tinted with rouge
Rose-stained skin, flushed like my cheeks
A crimson river, surging through my system
Blossoming from between my legs
Into bouquets of red tulips
Blemishing the new sheets, I bought last week
Now reeking of iron, like copper coins

Incessant rains, falling in hues of vermillion,
Caused by fierce thunderstorms,
Wreaking havoc on my inner rhythm
Pushing against the walls of my stomach;
Resembling an inflated balloon on the verge of popping

The ocean tides, killing me on the inside,
As they promise a new life
While I shed blood cells that count up to millions
Faithfully each month
Skin, laced with platelets
Coarse from the dried marrow
My body is a warrior, my blood holy

Emotions, forming a complex harmonic motion
Transforming into turbulent billows
Disrupting my peace and sanity

Quickly shape-shifting into
Loose waves, gently caressing the shore
I continue to shed my insides.
I am a daughter of Eve,
The forbidden child,
Bearing the curse of a poisoned cradle,
And a womb that grows blooming flowers.

MEET THE AUTHORS

Alexis M. Romo

Alexis M. Romo, a self-proclaimed "Flawed Artist," realized at a young age that her true passion lies in the arts, especially writing. Alexis has published two poetry and prose chapbooks: "The Maze to my Heart" (2020) and "The Bad, The Awful, The Shitty" (2018). She graduated from the University of Arizona in 2018, studying Psychology and Philosophy, and is an advocate for mental health and education. Alexis is currently working on becoming a writing teacher so she may combine her love for writing with her love for education. She currently resides in Arizona, where she continues to indulge in her passion for creating, as well as continuously fuelling her never-ending curiosity.

Aparna Goswami

A second-year law student, Aparna Goswami is a passionate advocate for human rights, equality, justice, and mental health. She writes both prose and poetry and wishes to become a distinguished writer one day. Would spend all her days drinking hot coffee, reading classic literature, and writing, if left uninterrupted.

Ann Chaiti Sarkar

Ann Chaiti Sarkar is a Senior-school English Teacher by profession. She chose this profession because of the following reason: The finest teacher she ever had was her Geography teacher in senior school. Though she favoured English and Economics to Geography, but her teacher was able to see past the figures and facts and make the subject resurrect beyond the basic curriculum. She was inspired by her teacher's maverick and pioneering techniques, and she always strives to induce the same concordant passion for innovative ways of teaching her students.

She reflects a heterogeneous personality including ambition, zeal, and the attributes of munificence, altruism, and thoughtfulness. She believes in fighting for what she deserves and has a fanatical passion for fashion and makeup. She started writing when she was a kid. Writing has always made her feel alive, exuberant, and pullulating her mind with unbridled ecstasy. As a young girl, she found herself in the stories she had written. Eventually, she began writing poems, love songs, and poems on dejection and endearments. She can burgeon her veiled emotions through her poetry and prose. She writes with fervour, expressing her sentiments with tenderness and brutality.

Alison Hawes

Ali started writing at a very young age and has always had a vivid imagination. When she's not writing, she can be found cooking, playing with her dog, Luca, or watching Grey's Anatomy.

Arti Chopra

Mrs. Arti Chopra belongs to the beautiful state of Jammu and Kashmir. After finishing her schooling in Jammu, she moved to Delhi to do a degree in Home Science. She married a fighter pilot while she was barely out of her teens, and subsequently, her life in the Airforce took her on interesting trips and postings all

over India and overseas. While her children were still young, she managed to add a B. Ed. Degree to her qualifications. The constant movement of the family did not support a career, but Arti taught in the Station schools wherever her husband was posted. All through this period she continued her passion for writing poetry and contributed regularly to magazines and journals. Being appalled at the lack of knowledge about life in the Armed Forces, in the minds of civilians, she has also written a book about life in the Indian Airforce by compiling various interesting anecdotes and travails of her life as an Airforce Officer's wife. She has written over five hundred poems on various topics and hopes to publish an anthology of her poems soon.

Aeryn Perez

Aeryn Perez is a young musician and writer living in France. Passionate about astrophysics and poetry, she shares contemplative writings on Instagram. Her poems are inspired by nature, dreams, and human relations.

Arunanshu Deep

Arunanshu Deep is an avid reader and a curious soul. That curiosity led him from reading to writing. Through his writing, he hopes to help others learn the joy of reading.

Annika Hauer

All her life, Annika Hauer has wanted to heal the hurting world through her writing. For years, she saw herself as the majority of us; we the cowards, the bystanders, the neutral. While the world seemed to burn around her, she found purpose in this anthology. She'd like to thank Ms. Sethi for pulling these fighters together, and thanks you for reading.

Bethany Rose Castle

Bethany Rose Castle is a passionate and empathetic soul who uses her words to make the world a better place. She is an advocate for human rights and uses her work to create strong political messages, through her poetry, artwork, and speechmaking. When she isn't making social commentaries, she is sharing her experiences of trauma, abuse, and anxiety in order to break the stigma.

Charlene Rosario

Charlene is an introverted tea drinker with a passion for good books and quotes that make your stomach drop. She loves night skies almost as much as she loves dogs. On good days, she's a writer.

Divya Bora

Divya Bora, by profession, is in the field of finance. Her work requires her to study legal terms and numbers. Due to her passion for words, she loves to write. Writing is her source of freedom. She believes that when one writes, subjective thoughts flow. She wishes to be the kind of writer that allows your mind to run free. She hopes that you enjoy her work, and wishes to see you in her next book.

Deepika Bhardwaj

Deepika Bhardwaj can usually be found reading a book, and that book will more likely than not be a poetry book. She is an MBBS student and has written various articles and poems on topics crucial to gender equality, communal harmony, mental health, and overpopulation. Being an author was always on her bucket list, and eventually, it became a reality. Granddaughter of a renowned journalist, late Mr. R.C Sharma, Deepika developed a knack for writing from him. She aspires to continue writing, as her way to contribute towards a greater change. Other books she has co-authored are 'The journey of self-romance', 'Coming of age', 'Aesthetics', and 'Tormented'.

Debjani Saha

Trapped in life's rhythmic meters, she is almost a prosaic perfection, well... almost, and yet her mind flies free, wandering around, like unrhymed poetry. A middle school teacher, a voracious reader, an animal lover, and somewhat of a poetess, she loves everything that wreaks thoughts. Hence, writing is her sole cathartic escape. Well, a pen has more patience than people, right? Please read her work and go figure her out.

Emily Alexander

Emily is a writer, wife, and mother raising babies and chasing cats in the rural Midwest. Her favourite parts of life include dark roast coffee, sunglasses, following Jesus, and her husband's cooking. Along with writing, she enjoys concocting new homemade skincare products, singing, and practicing for her future as a Rockstar. A medical lab scientist by training and a free spirit by heart, she is not only a creative but also a voice for the introverts. She has a passion for supporting mental health and human rights through poetry, personal stories, and above all else, love.

Eileen Salisbury

Eileen writes short poetry on themes of love, hope, loss, resilience, and finding beauty in fleeting moments. She lives in Brisbane, Australia, with her two young children and works part-time as a librarian.

Harshita Garrepalli

Harshita is an ardent writer who believes in the power of emotions—and that writing not only aids self-expression but helps in feeling complex emotions. That as soon as something is written, its importance multiples. She hopes to change the world as much as she can through her work, to relate to someone, to possibly make someone smile, cry—feel. Harshita wants to give her readers a holistic experience while also obliging them to think, and she hopes you enjoy reading what she has written for you. You can connect with her on Instagram at @quillixr.

Heer Dayani

Heer likes writing about a lot of topics that aren't confined to a particular genre. She basically avoids human interaction as much as possible. She is pretty fluent in sarcasm and rhyming words. Solitude and sleep are her best friends.

Jagruthi Kommuri

K. Jagruthi is an e-commerce graduate and an MBA student, who started writing to express her feelings. She loves to write to ignite a little hope and faith in the reader. She's a simple girl who finds solace in words and writes to spread love and positivity in the world. She believes kindness goes a long way when communicated through the heart.

Jacqueline Olivia

Jacqueline Olivia Collins (better known as Jacqueline Olivia) is a dedicated writer, poet, and author of her debut poetry collection, "The Girl with a Maze for a Mind". She currently works as a writer and is pursuing an Advertising and Marketing Communications major at the Fashion Institute of Technology, with hopes that her newfound knowledge will further develop her career.

Jennifer Meyers

Jennifer is a wild spirit, who loves to embrace her creativity by fashion, modelling, and design. Her mother was a writer all throughout her life and she's excited to embrace her own writing journey and connect with like-minded people.

Jesika Gaston

Jesika Gaston is a 21-year-old poet, born and raised in the Central Valley. Though she is a poet, she writes fictional pieces as well. She loves the rain, long car rides, seeing people smile, and hopes they can find pieces of themselves inside of her words.

Kristina Kerber

Kristina Kerber, working under the pseudonym Artemis, is a 20-year-old poet and novelist. She has previously been published in several anthologies as well as literary magazines such as "Eve Poetry Magazine". Her educational background in English and Psychology has given her a broad base from which to approach many

topics. Additional to pursuing her studies, she is writing and editing for her university's newspaper. Samples of her previously unpublished work can be found on her Instagram account, @alliterative_artemis.

Kriti

Kriti is a twenty-one-year-old finance professional. Till the time a story is intriguing to her, the genre doesn't matter. One such fascinating mythological tale inspired her to write her first story years ago. She lost her touch with writing outweighed by her ambitions but now, coming back to it has made her happier than ever.

Mythili M. U

Mythili M. U is a fifteen-year-old high school student, a poet, and an ardent athlete living in India. In her free time, she enjoys reading a good book, listening to her favorite playlists, grooving on upbeat music, and/or taking a nap. She's also an admitted sports fanatic and enjoys watching football, cricket, badminton, and athletics over the weekend.

Greek mythology and history intrigue her young mind, and you can discover some references of the same in her writing.

Madhurya Kommuri

Madhurya is an aspiring psychologist by profession and a poet by passion. A perfect imperfection, a beautiful mess is what defines her the best. Bringing out the stories people bury inside with patience and comforting, soothing poetry is her little way of bringing peace to minds and making the world a better place for people.

Marissa Kovalenko

Marissa Kovalenko was born in Portland, Oregon, and raised in the Pacific Northwest where she currently resides with her family. Her life-long passions include poetry, literature, fine arts, and graphic arts. Marissa believes there is no greater expression of oneself than through the arts, and because of this; she started her Instagram page displaying art and poetry in May of 2020. If you'd like to view more of her work, you can do so at @m.e.verse on Instagram.

Noela Paraschiv

Noela Paraschiv is a fiery, empathetic soul from Romania and the author of *"Self-Transcending"*, a collection of poetry focusing on growth and all the things that come with it. In her search for the truth and for the meaning of life, she fell in love with writing, philosophy, spirituality, and art. Her main goal in life is to impact people in a positive way and leave a mark on this world.

Nagasri MN

Nagasri is multi-talented. She would choose the right words to express her thoughts, not just her thoughts, she would also do the writing when she is made aware of the feelings a person is going through. Not just writing, she can sketch and paint abstractly as well. You can check out her work on her Instagram page, @the_artification.

Noelle Nams

Noelle Nams is a creative communicator, writer, and public speaker. She published her first book "It's all bcoz of you"- a romantic fiction novel, 8 years ago at the age of 22. Her second book "Unconditional"- a collection of 101 eternal love poems came out recently in August 2020. She is a social activist who has worked with NGOs like Teach for India, and Junior Achievement USA. She has also been a TEDx organizer. She loves exploring nature and different cultures. She also enjoys reading, cooking, gardening, and various craft projects in her leisure time. You can reach out to her at: inoellenams@gmail.com

Neha Mazumder

Neha's creative mind is trapped inside her technical brain and is always trying to find new ways to express its heap of emotions. Currently, in a war between mind and brain, art and science, Neha is exploring, learning, writing, daring to live freely.

Omaira Mahan

Omaira Mahan began her writing journey on Wattpad, where she completed her first novel (Focus). She is very fond of poetry and was inspired by Edgar Allan Poe's work to begin writing her own. When she is not writing, Mahan runs her own online business where she sells beauty products and home decor called Shabnum Shoppe Beauty. She is currently attending California State University, Northridge as a Political Science major.

Padmini Peteri

Padmini Peteri is an avid reader who has a passion for writing her heart out. She writes short stories and poetry in both Hindi and English languages. To her, writing is healing and a way of expression. She mostly writes about mental health and social issues. She gets lost in the world of books, of imagination, of poetry, and stories. She  believes that smiling and spreading happiness makes the world a better place to live in. Her writing finds wings at her Instagram handle @minithoughts_pp.

Robert Ormsby

 Robert Ormsby is a Canadian born/American raised writer, currently residing in South Carolina. Robert is the author of the #DistractionAction series, which takes an honest and introspective look at mental health in an attempt to help others find comfort and strength in discussing their own issues.

Rhea Choudhury

Rhea believes in writing from experience because giving words to one's experience is therapeutic and genuine. No writing is good or bad; it is just that what you already know was felt for the first time by someone else. She appreciates romance and she's pretty easily awed by how writers define their version of love.

Sybil Samuel

She's a dreamer, artist, overthinker, a misfit with an insatiable quest to read and write. She loves music, movies, travelling, and exploring new things. She doesn't believe in perfection because many times, it is imperfection that paints the perfect story. Her blogs are:

www.thethirteenthpage.blogspot.com | www.crimsonredink.blogspot.in | www.sybilsamuel1303.wordpress.com

Shama Mahajan

An aspiring lawyer who spends most of the time inside her head (a fancy way of saying "Introvert") but who enjoys performing on stage. A bibliophile who finds solace and voice in poetry and enjoys the power it wields. For whom poetry is a culmination of thoughts stimulated by personal feelings, opinions, and surrounding events. A staunch believer that, family and friends are the best company to spend time with. A tea addict with extremely low self-control when it comes to binge-watching web-series, hence, prefer movies. One who prefers to follow passion along with career.

Shakira Washington

Shakira began her writing journey in February 2020 to challenge herself to be more creative. Since then, she started her Instagram page for her writings and published her first novella. Shakira wants to bring the nuanced experiences of Black Women to the page.

Skyler Saunders

Skyler Saunders is a recent UC Berkeley graduate with a Bachelor of Arts in Sociology. They are originally from Shasta County in Northern California but now live in Los Angeles. You can find Skyler's poetry on their Instagram @smilingatmysandwich, where they are embarking on a challenge to write a poem every day for an entire year. In  their free time, they enjoy reading, acting, and creating digital art. Skyler's pronouns are she/her or they/them.

Shaymi Shah

Shaymi Shah is a freelance architect by profession and a creative content writer by passion. Most of her writing comes from her observations of everyday life. She tends to have an inclination towards seeing the otherwise common things that happen in life with a different perspective. She believes that life is as natural as anything gets and there's no way of really writing about it aptly with utmost detail- one just has to experience it and live in the moments.

Swati Thapa

We go through many different phases in life and with each phase, we go through different emotions, pain, happiness. Swati likes to think of herself as an expressionist and seeks to express these emotions in the simplest way possible, making it relatable to anyone who goes through her writings. Weaving together words and unravelling

emotions close to the heart by keeping it simple and real.

Sharron Green

Sharron Green is from Guildford, England, and is present as @rhymes_n_roses on Instagram. She enjoys sharing her poetry which attempts to make sense of modern life. Sharron has self-published a book of rhymes titled "Introducing Rhymes_n_Roses", and will soon have a chapbook of Lockdown Poetry as well as poems in over ten other international anthologies. She has recently relaunched her website https://rhymesnroses.com and is studying for an MA in Creative Writing. The poem, 'Speak Up!' is a collaboration with Avi Baidya, a friend from Guildford, a keen rugby fan and champion of diversity in our community.

s.h.

s.h. is a high school student who wants the world to feel through her words. Some of her hobbies are reading, singing, and dancing. She has big hopes for her future and determination for achieving it all.

Snehal Agarwal

Snehal Agarwal is a 21-year-old Chartered Accountant from Mumbai. She is talkative, a sitcom fanatic, and secretly, a nerd. Her stories are a reflection of events commonly occurring around us, yet ignored by most. She wishes to make a change in society, one day at a time.

Sameem Hassain Mohammad

Sameem Hassain Mohammad is a fighter of depression; hails from Kakinada, Andhra Pradesh, presently working in the marketing field. He is a lover of books, cinema, and music. He considers storytelling as ultimate blissfulness. You can follow him on Instagram at @sameem_hassain.

Tanisha Thalnerkar

Tanisha, eighteen, is a high school graduate and is yet to spread her wings to fly off to college. As this year has been a struggle for everyone, she strives to make it through even stronger. Hence, she started confiding in expressing through writing and started her own Instagram page, @ll.deardiary.ll where she could be heard through her words about anything and everything, being that her muse. Tanisha, as she says, just doesn't want to become an ordinary person in an ordinary world. Rather, she wants to be the change, to make a difference in this world, and to contribute in making the world great again.

Tolulope Ibiyode

Tolu enjoys writing. If he isn't writing poetry, he is writing codes. He writes about life in general, which includes, but is not limited to, social issues, love, technology, himself, God. His main goal of writing is to motivate and uplift his readers.

Tiffany Lindfield

Tiffany Lindfield is a social worker by day, trade, and heart working as an advocate for climate justice, gender equality, and animal rights. By night, she is a prolific reader of anything decent and a writer.

Usama Bin Tanveer

Usama Bin Tanveer is an emerging poet cum writer, with over 55 poems and modest contributions to the field of prose writing. He is a Legal Practitioner with Legal as well as Managerial Qualifications from the University of Punjab, Lahore, Pakistan. For him, aesthetic writings are not limited to literature graduates only, as literature is an open field for all to play on.

Uniliar

Uniliar loves discovering and learning from the many literature arts, using writing to escape and advocate for various societal challenges. She constantly reads and explores past collections of classics and applies the inspiration to create her own unique style of written words. Currently studying in high school, Uniliar wishes to pursue a career in stem while further improving her interest and written expression in poetry, hoping to inspire other creators to start their artistic journeys as well.

Urmi Chakraborty

Urmi has been writing since she was a little girl. For a long time, she had kept her poems concealed in diaries and scraps of paper everywhere but a couple of years back, after getting inspired by a friend, she started her own Instagram page where she began posting her poetry and write-ups. Since then, she has put forward more than 600 of her oeuvres.  She mainly writes about the ebb and flow of life and her tone is deliciously dark. At times, when she doesn't write, she likes to read and let herself loose in words. The first poem she wrote was about her grandfather who is very dear to her heart. She makes her home in Kolkata, India with her family, a small undisciplined bookshelf, and a rising number of incomplete writing projects.

Yashika Tomar

 Yashika is from India. Pursuing research in the field of literature, she has been scribbling for quite a while now, weaving her words, at times recklessly, at times with profound grace, yet sometimes like a kid trying to make the world believe in fairies, shooting stars, unicorns, and ghosts, even. She's inspired by poets like Plath, Dickinson, Dylan, Milton, Frost along with many others. She believes reading is instrumental in building one's character along with expressing oneself in countless ways. She says, "The fact that every person breathes a dire urge to be heard, makes my ink bleed on the innocent blank sheets".

OUR STORY

We're all on a journey, and our 'writers' have made it beautiful.

A dreamcatcher is an object made with feathers and strings, essentially used as lucky charms in many parts of the world. In the same way, Inkfeathers brings together writers, editors, and artists together to form a dreamcatcher that works in favour of the young writers and readers and if you're positive about it, it may bring you luck as well.

We at Inkfeathers are connected to thousands of writers globally, who believe in the magic of telling stories. This stream of connectivity with the writers, the fact that everyone has a unique detail or edge to their story makes Inkfeathers proud to partner with these young literary as well as collaborative minds.

Back in 2013, our founders came together to form an offline group for their love of literature, and this formed collaborative energy with many young literature-wounded minds which eventually led these offline meetings to stand-ups, storytelling events, poetry slams, meet-ups to share experiences, and many other things. In 2016, Inkfeathers finally launched as the brand project under one Private Limited Company. This expanded opportunity gave a number of possibilities and a new way to expand our support for writers.

This dream of wanting to bring together writers as well as readers has come true beyond measure as writers connect to us from countries like United States, United Kingdom, Canada each day to bring their stories to life.

As of this year, we are extremely delighted to provide you our website (www.inkfeathers.com) where all your queries can be resolved about our self-publishing process and latest anthologies. You can get hold of the latest updates on anthologies, events, offers, new book releases and so much more here. You can go ahead and order a book from our bookstore to get a taste of our mindful curation of stories and poems.

Inkfeathers Publishing family encourages you to really put your feelings out there in words for the world to see, in order to have a common ground to grow mutually. We are a creative platform for all those seeking literary help in terms of having their words published.

Believe us, publishing a book is not easy, but we come to a writer's rescue at each phase of having their book in print in terms of Editing, Designing, Branding, Marketing, and all the other work that goes behind until you have a printed copy in your hands for Distribution. Together, it couldn't have been any easier. We will be there for you, to help you turn your manuscript into a freshly bound book that sells off the glass bookshelves.

With Love,
Inkfeathers Publishing

INKFEATHERS PUBLISHING

India's Most Author Friendly Publishing House

Stay updated about latest books, anthologies, events, exclusive offers, contests, product giveaways and other things that we do to support authors.

 Inkfeathers Publishing

 @InkfeathersPublishing

 @_Inkfeathers

 @Inkfeathers

 Inkfeathers.com

We'd love to connect with you!